THE MAGNETIC EFFECT

Books by
Albert Roy Davis and Walter C. Rawls, Jr.

The Magnetic Blueprint of Life

The Rainbow in Your Hands

The Magnetic Effect

Magnetism and Its Effects on the Living System

THE MAGNETIC EFFECT

Albert Roy Davis
&
Walter C. Rawls, Jr.

Acres U.S.A.

First Printing, 1975
Ninth Printing, 1999

Library of Congress Catalog Card Number 93-72037

ISBN: 0-911311-17-3

Printed in the United States of America

CONTENTS

NEW CONCEPTS AND APPLICATIONS

The research findings disclosed in this book are directed to actual results obtained that can be duplicated by any qualified man or woman who is equipped to do so at any time and at any suitable location. This book is a result of experiments from research that have been duplicated by members of the research and development divisions within the scientific community. This book is also presented as a scientific paper on the results obtained by this development in and of the application and understanding in part of applied magnetic (biomagnetic) energies.

Research findings presented apply for lower to higher forms of animals and living biological systems.

The Authors

SPECIAL RESEARCH ACKNOWLEDGMENTS

We wish to give special recognition to the following men for their outstanding research reproductions of the findings presented in this book.

DR. RALPH U. SIERRA
of the
Puerto Rico Scientific Research Laboratory

and

DR. YOSHIO SEKI
of the
Magna International Laboratory
Tokyo, Japan

DR. RALPH U. SIERRA

Dr. Sierra is the director of the Puerto Rico Scientific Research Laboratory located at 1707 Arkansas Street, San Gerardo, Rio Piedras, Puerto Rico 00926.

More than anyone else, Dr. Sierra has duplicated the research outlined in this book. He was the first scientist, independent of our laboratories, to research magnetic field applications to water (1969), using the separate pole concept, in Puerto Rico and South America. He has designed and constructed many instruments for polarizing minerals in water. His work in stimulating the hydrogen complex of water has resulted in new approaches for a better understanding in this field of magnetic research.

Although the majority of the scientific community today believes the energies of a magnet or electromagnet are homogeneous (the same), our laboratory discovered in 1936 that each pole's energies are opposite in effects and biological potential. Our and Dr. Sierra's research on the two separate pole energies are closely bound together. In duplicating our research, Dr. Sierra has developed many new concepts in magnetic energy controls in research with large and small animals. Further, Dr. Sierra's work in seed stimulation by magnetic energies has resulted in one of Puerto Rico's finest natural gardens.

It has been our pleasure to work with such a fine and dedicated man and research scientist for many years. Dr. Sierra's family has been of great help and encouragement in this important science.

The Authors

DR. YOSHIO SEKI

Dr. Seki is the director of the Magna International Laboratory located at Sakai 3-9-11, Musashino-Shi, Tokyo, Japan.

Dr. Seki was a member of a delegation researching biomagnetic sciences that visited our laboratories a few years ago.

Upon his return to Japan, Dr. Seki undertook to reproduce a number of our research findings on living systems, including our findings on seed stimulation. He has undertaken the establishment of a world trade information center to distribute information on biomagnetics. He has also been instrumental in introducing our work into Japan, Australia and other countries.

In recognizing the importance of the separate pole concept and its potential benefits to humanity, Dr. Seki's work to establish a better scientific climate for the acceptance of these discoveries and applications is worthy of commendation.

It is our pleasure to work with such a dedicated scientist and his talented and wonderful family in the establishment of biomagnetics for the betterment of humanity.

The Authors

ACKNOWLEDGMENTS

For duplication of our research findings in support of this scientific disclosure. Their untiring efforts and dedication have been outstanding contributions.

Dr. and Mrs. Robert J. Morgan
Dr. Frederick Doughty Beck
Dr. Ruth W. Emerson
Dr. and Mrs. Harold Brownlee
Dr. Glenn E. Trager
Dr. Leslie O. Korth, London, England
Dr. Leonard J. Allan, Kent, England
Dr. E. W. Hinson, London, England

To the memory of Dr. N. S. Hanaka, one of the world's most dedicated men, who spent his life researching all aspects of the field of Natural Sciences. Dr. Hanaka's work with us in this field cannot be described in words. His special research into the dental aspects of biomagnetics is an outstanding contribution to his love of all mankind. Mrs. Hanaka's support to her husband's work was very encouraging.

Associated Doctors and Technicians of the Tehmatbi Vadnagarwala Hospital, Calcutta, India.

Dr. Julius Soled
Dr. Ed Stadel
Dr. Barbara Slof
Dr. Mary Mayer

For assistance and dedication in our research:

Mr. Orlando Cepeda
Mr. and Mrs. Donald Larsen and Family
(Roger, Donald, Sue, Krystal and James)
Mr. and Mrs. Chester Hurlbut
Mr. and Mrs. Robert K. Leonard

PREFACE

This book is written to introduce the science of applying a magnet's energies to the animal system. Biomagnetics, the biological use of magnetism, is destined to become a foremost medical and biological applied science.

This natural science can be used in emergency or wartime conditions where medical or professional care is not immediately obtainable. In our research with animals we have found that a basic knowledge in the application of magnetic energy can render significant aid in relieving complaints. No drugs, chemicals or surgery procedures are required with a thorough understanding in applying this science.

The material in this book is not offered as a course of treatment but as a scientific paper in book form. This is the first presentation of many of our experiments, conducted with the proper controls, that provide research findings reproducible anywhere, anytime, by any person who is properly equipped.

The Albert Roy Davis Laboratories have supplied advice, instructions, and new instrumentation to doctors and scientists in many nations of the world for more than 30 years. Hundreds of scientists, young and old, have reproduced a number of our discoveries. This reproduction by other scientists, in their independent manner, supports the facts as we have found them to be, and which we present in the following pages. In all our initial experiments, controls as norms were used in relation to the treated subject, and any new discovery was duplicated hundreds of times for computer-exact results.

In this new scientific breakthrough to an ancient science, magnetism is the basis for still greater discoveries in all fields of applied sciences, including electronics, electromagnetics, chemistry, physics, atomic energy, radiological applied sciences, and medical instrument design.

Although there are many applications forthcoming to industrial use with these new breakthroughs, the more readily apparent applications are in the natural health and medical areas. They include pain control instrumentations, infection arrest, cancer arrest of many forms and types, if not all forms and types, and arrest, control and immunity of many other diseases that are problems to humanity.

Far-thinking men and women are now applying these new discoveries, and their number will continue to increase in the future.

Producing more and better food products is another area where the reader will see this science successfully applied in the future. Those persons in authority who move too slowly will find that public pressure demands a new look in this science. The more the public can know about magnetism and its effects, properly understood and applied, the more effective the adaptation will become in the beneficial applications of magnetic energy, a natural energy for the benefit of all humanity.

The Authors

INTRODUCTION

The knowledge of the effects of applying magnetism generated and transmitted from a magnet is not new. It may be older than the ancient art of acupuncture. Records continue to be found showing knowledge of magnetism and acupuncture existing ever earlier in the history of humanity on this earth.

The Greek physician Galen, in his ninth book, *De Simplicium Medicamentorum Facultatibus,* mentions the use of magnetism in healing as early as 200 B.C. Galen describes his early research with magnetism as an outstanding "purgative."

The famous Persian physician, Ali Abbas, in about A.D. 1000, describes his findings in using magnetism to relieve disorders as "spasms" and "gout."

In the sixteenth century A.D., Paracelsus, physician and alchemist, wrote of his work in relieving conditions of "hernias, dropsy, and jaundice" with magnetic applications. We also find the writings of Ambroise Pare describing how physicians took lodestone, a natural magnet, ground it into fine powder, and mixed it with "pappe" to be taken internally. The magnetic powder mixed with honey was applied to external openings, wounds, ruptures, and "other forms" of human ailments.

The basis of this sixteenth-century practice is now in use in the most modern laboratories and hospitals in Israel. During the past few years scientists and medical persons in Israel have mixed medicines and antibiotics with magnetic powder. The patient takes the mixture orally. Then a magnet is applied to the outside of the body for direction to that area in need of medication. The magnet then holds the medication in that specific area for a better effect from the medication. This is an improvement over the sixteenth-century method, yet is still a crude means, when we consider the beneficial effects obtained by direct application of the North or South pole of a magnet for a desired result. With a proper knowledge of magnetism, the separate pole effect, our extended and conclusive research findings on animals show we can use the proper pole energy of a magnet to provide desired results, internally or externally, with the animal body. These findings, in part, we will present in this publication.

The lack of serious interest in Biomagnetics by leading scientists and authorities in the United States is well documented. From our own records we have, for more than 30 years, communicated detailed scientific papers showing reproducible evidence to many members of the scientific and government community. We have been gratified by the many far-thinking scientists, other professional and nonprofessional persons, who believe in our work. We regret that the proper authorities have not acted as they should to investigate and adapt our scientific breakthroughs. A number of scientists, as well as other authorities, say they are not interested or they just don't believe it. They dismiss these new scientific discoveries with an old worn-out textbook adage that "magnetism does not act in any way to stimulate or regress the activities of human cells." Some will not read our research reports. Others, after reading the reports, will deny them without scientifically reproducing the experiments we offer in proof. They will not lift their fingers to advance their knowledge of this important science. This is the state of the scientific art found in our nation today, a nation now only seventh at best in scientific leadership of the world. How long will this condition be tolerated? When more fair-minded persons see and understand the true facts about magnetic energy, the great benefits to humanity cannot continue to be denied. Proper recognition will lead to proper adaptation. This book is presented to show and provide reproducible experiments and findings with animal research that, with proper use as indicated, will produce computer-exact results on living systems, and even on water, by the use of controlled magnetic fields of natural energy.

All new discoveries, applications, and understandings presented are by Albert Roy Davis or were developed under his guidance and supervision from the Albert Roy Davis Scientific Laboratories in Green Cove Springs, Florida. We look forward to the increased use of natural energy for a more natural environment, The Magnetic Age.

The Authors

THE MAGNETIC EFFECT

CHAPTER 1

THE EFFECTS OF MAGNETIC FIELDS ON ANIMAL SYSTEMS

In undertaking the study or research of any science the professional or nonprofessional must have some knowledge of why things happen, not simply that they do happen.

Biomagnetics is the study of the effects of a magnet's energies on the biological system. It is not associated with any radio frequency, instrumental method of producing radio waves, diathermy, or any other form of electromagnetic energy. A magnet's two types of energies, its two poles, North and South, present two completely different forms of energy when applied to a biological system.

If we take a sample of animal or human blood and spin off the fluids, the plasma, and leave only the red blood cells, then place these red blood cells on a slide and insert it into a good microscope, when we bring a magnet under the slide the red blood cells all spin around and point in one direction. This is the polarization, alignment, of the iron and ions in the red blood cells. When you align any form of energy, as in the red blood cells experiment, you have gathered strength, power and energy, amassing a separated random energy into a condition where that energy is brought together to become a higher level of energy.

What happens when a magnet's energies are applied to arrest certain diseases, for example, on laboratory rats with cancer or leukemia? These conditions have been arrested by a magnet's energies. The Kathy Solis presentation before the American Medical Association confirmed this result from actual visual and biological tests, as described in *Prevention* in February, 1973.

After only four years of exposing many animals to magnetic fields, this young scientist presented the following facts: When the affected animals were exposed to 3,000 gauss magnets (using both poles), the erythrocytes in peripheral blood were increased while the number of leukocytes was reduced. This arrested the cancerous condition in part. However, when the animals were removed from the influence by the magnet's poles, the cancer condition increased.

Our research shows that this presentation used too much time exposure to the cancer condition, and that the use of a magnet's energies without the separate pole effect is incorrect. We will present in this research publication the facts that have been duplicated thousands of times that prove each pole of the magnet has a singular effect. The proper application to the specific condition can control many complaints effectively.

CHAPTER II

SUMMARY OF PRIOR RESEARCH REPORT NO. 1

The effects of a magnet's energies on animals and living systems and the outstanding results obtained in this research resulted in the title of "Biomagnetism." "Bio" is used to define biological, and "magnetism" is defined in this science as magnetic fields generated by a magnet.

Refraining from involvement in the physics of magnetism, to present the basic values in a more readable fashion, our attention will be directed to practical and technical research with magnetic fields. A more technical view of this science is available in our earlier book, *Magnetism and Its Effects on the Living System* (Hicksville, New York: Exposition Press, 1974).

The science of Biomagnetism, also called Biomagnetics, is often misunderstood, and knowledge of it is limited. Now that interest and research are increasing in many nations of the world, we wish to remove some basic misunderstandings regarding this form of all natural energy. Outstanding scientists and researchers, universities and colleges, remain incorrect to this day in on biological systems. Technical books in general use their basic knowledge of the effects of magnetic fields today, in all countries of the world, continue to describe the two poles of a magnet as homogeneous in nature and effects.

The truth of the matter is that a magnet provides two dissimilar forms of energy coming from the two separate poles of any magnet, or type of material, that will present the two basic energies as we know them to be.

These two energies are generally known as the North pole and the South pole of a magnet. A number of years ago we isolated the two poles and measured their effects on biological systems. We found that living systems presented a different reaction to each pole. There was a great difference between these two poles, long thought of as being the same. The common theory, we found, was in fact totally incorrect. Later we were able to support this discovery technically by the actual measurement of the direction of the electron spin that is transmitted from the two poles of all magnets.

Further, the direction of the movement of the electrons (magnetic energy) in the North and South poles was reverse in nature. In fact, the energy coming from the South pole of a magnet moved, traveled and took on a spinning vortex of energy to the right or clockwise; while that energy coming from the North pole of a magnet spun, moved and cycled to the left or counterclockwise.

This discovery was not confirmed officially until the development of the present space age and the actual magnetic measurements that were made by complex technical magnetometers from space. The energy of a magnet, like that of the earth's two magnetic poles, the North and South poles, does not simply leave one pole and travel around the magnet to reenter the other end of the magnet, but on leaving the South pole it travels only halfway around the magnet to its center. Here it alters its electronic spin, taking on a reverse spin and resultant form of energy, and leaves the center of the magnet or earth to continue on reentering the North pole of the magnet or earth, as the case may be.

Published space research reports now prove this to be fact. Direct and provable knowledge exists on the division of the earth's own magnetic energy. When we apply this knowledge to a bar or cylinder magnet, we find that the same law allows us better to research and understand this form of natural electronic energy.

Before these confirmations of our research findings were made we developed a method of photographing the invisible lines of force that are transmitted from the two poles of a magnet. By this development we proved that the two poles are totally different in nature. We were able to see the two spinning vortexes of magnetic energy and examine them in detail. This photographic system in color was made possible by the use of a cathode ray vacuum tube and the directions of the magnet's singular placed poles to the cathode ray sweep. This resulted in the photographic visual display of the magnet's two forms of energies.

It was during these periods of biomagnetic research that the separate effects of the two poles of a magnet on living systems were discovered. The different effects on a biological system with the separate pole use furnishes reproducible proof of this discovery.

BASIC EARLY EXPERIMENTS

It was soon found that a common horseshoe magnet was worthless for this research work. The poles of a horseshoe magnet are physically too close together to allow research use of either of the two poles as a separate and different energy.

It was then necessary to develop and use a long straight magnet having the two poles, the North and the South, at each of the well-separated ends of this type of metal or composition magnet. We could then apply either pole only to fluids, seeds or animals, and record the effects of only the one pole of that magnet without the interference of the other pole, which would occur in the use of the horseshoe magnet.

The first series of experiments dealt with animals and seeds only. Following this came research into fluids, the upgrading of proteins, vital acids, and food values using the two separate poles of a suitable long magnet. It was soon discovered that the South pole energies of a magnet were positive in electrical nature and transmitted a positive effect to living systems. This applied to seeds, which are a form of life, and the lower types of animals such as mice, rats, and species of fish.

Additional experiments, with proper controls, duplicated hundreds of times, increased our knowledge that the North pole of the magnet presented a negative electronic energy, thus a negative effect to the biological subject, whereas the South pole presented a positive energy, thus a positive effect to the living system.

EARLIER RESULTS ON SEEDS, PLANTS, AND ANIMALS

Some of the first applications researched on the separate pole effect of a magnet to living systems resulted in findings on seeds. When seeds were placed within the energies of the South pole of a magnet for several hours—from six to 81 to 200 hours—then planted, they presented an improved growth, hardier plants and increased yield of products, as in the case of vegetable seeds. If we used the North pole of the magnet to treat the seeds, they developed into thin, tall plants with poor vegetables when grown to maturity. This was noted in the stages of primary growth when comparing the plants with similar untreated seeds. The untreated seeds and plants served as controls. Controls were used in all our experiments for comparing results on treated seeds.

In laboratory analysis, examinations of the vital life-support biochemicals of the leaves, stems and the end product, we found that the protein, sugars and oils in vegetables were higher in the plants treated with the South pole of the magnet than the untreated or control plant products. The analysis showed that plants and their products grown from seeds treated with the North pole of the magnet were lower in vital life biochemicals.

The food product results were lower in protein, sugars, and oils than the untreated seed plants or control plants. The untreated seed plants acted as a guide in comparing the end results of these experiments, which took a number of years to complete.

Treating sugar beets with the South pole energies resulted in a greater production of natural sugars. Treating peanuts with the South pole produced more natural peanut oils and protein contents.

Not content with these findings, we turned our research to small creatures such as earthworms. It was found that when baby worms were exposed to the South pole energy after birth they grew larger and stronger than the untreated control worms. Hundreds of tests were run. The results were similar to the treating of seeds by the separate poles of the magnet. Because earthworms are 90 percent protein, on average, further evidences of the effects of the South or positive energy of the magnet showed in the marked increase of protein from the common earthworms in their biological protein structures.

The same pattern of research was then undertaken on larger creatures in the mouse and the rat families. Again, the South pole positive results were noted in larger and healthier rodents and their offspring. These research experiments over a number of years presented further proof that the right-hand spin of electrons provided by the South pole of a magnet increased the vital life biochemical strength of all animals in this research.

CHAPTER III

SUMMARY OF PRIOR RESEARCH REPORT NO. 2

Direction of the North pole energies to the system arrested life, and slowed maturity, growth, and development of all life systems exposed to this negative electronic field.

These major breakthroughs presented the possibility of the development through additional research of new and vitally important uses for this energy in the field of medical research.

If we pause for a moment and study the separate effects of a magnet's poles, we will see that they could be used to contain and arrest many difficult disorders that the medical profession and medical researchers find very difficult to arrest or control.

We have directed our research toward the control of many types of diseases and other biological living system complaints. We feel that foremost of all work we have accomplished is arresting the spread of cancer cells in animal research. Although this appeared to be the most difficult of our research undertakings, it proved to be one of our most important discoveries. We were able to obtain a number of live cancer tissues. It is necessary to infect a local area of a living system before a transplant of live cancer tissue can be made to take and form the first stages of a cancer condition. We found it is impossible to transplant live cancer tissue cells to a healthy animal, because the cancer cells will not multiply or take in healthy tissue. After infecting the tissue of mice, rats and other animals, it was possible to have the live transplanted cancer tissue cells take and form a small infectionlike tumor. Before proceeding, it is well to remember that there are more than 100 types and kinds of cancers known at this time. Making a blanket statement that all cancers can be arrested by any method known depends on the availability of all these types and transplants, magnetic exposure made, and the results noted.

We will contain our remarks to our known research only. In the primary to advanced cancer types, classified 1, 2, 3, 4, A, B, C, D, the condition has been arrested by the application of the North pole negative energy. After a transplant of cancer growth to the animal, suitable time was allowed to pass for noticeable growth of the cancer through cell destruction and the forming of cancer tumors. The condition was arrested to a point where the animal's own system took control, producing necessary normal cells to overcome the cell breakdown effects of the cancer.

Prior to this undertaking of cancer control research, it appeared that available types and kinds of magnets were not suitable for this work to obtain desired results.

Research was undertaken to design a special type and kind of magnet to allow better application of separate pole energy to the animal system.

TYPE AND PLACEMENT OF MAGNET

The use of a horseshoe magnet is not accurate for this research. A better separation of the North and South pole energies is necessary. A flat slatelike magnet was designed that allowed 3000 gauss averages over extended lengths of time with little loss of energy. Gauss is the unit of magnetism, as volt is the unit of measuring voltage. The N-1 type of biomagnet was constructed and used in this research.

The N-1 biomagnet now used in most of our research is the magnet cited in the following research case reports in this book. It is approximately six inches long by two inches wide by one-half inch thick. It is nonmetal. The composition is ferric materials mixed with a gray-black coloring material that gives the appearance of slate. Although the magnet will break on dropping or rough handling, its value is greater for this research than that of the metal type of magnets. Approximately 3000 gauss is used. The life of the magnet is from three to five years, and it can be recharged again and again if needed.

In the placement of this magnet to the research subject as described in this book, the North pole or the South pole, a separate side of this magnet, is applied directly in contact with the skin of the animal over that part or segment desired to arrest or increase a condition.

Having two flat surfaces, one North pole and the other South pole, allows the use of all South pole energy or all North pole energy as desired upon the paws, limbs, or sections of the animal body. For identification we mark the South pole of the N-1 biomagnet with red paint or fingernail polish. The North pole side we leave unmarked.

Although it is not general knowledge, animals suffer many complaints similar to humans, accompanied by pain and limiting physical abilities.

CHAPTER IV

RESEARCH APPLICATIONS

APPENDIX

Many animals, like man, suffer from infections, swellings and stoppages in the passage to the appendix. This body part is a long slender outgrowth at the opening of the large intestine. Appendicitis is the inflammation of the vermiform appendix, a small saclike appendage of the large intestine.

Applying the North pole energy to the infected or inflamed area 45 minutes to one hour twice or three times a day shows a marked reduction. This is especially accurate if application is started soon after tenderness or pain is noted. In animal research, including large animals, the North pole energy not only arrests the condition but also sedates the pain. Time and number of applications depend, as in most conditions, on the advancement of the condition.

The accepted procedure is to operate and remove this section of the body as soon as it shows any difficulties. This part of the body is considered worthless, resulting in a lack of interest in keeping the appendix in the body. However, a number of research reports indicate that this part of the body partially provides certain fluids to defend the body against forms of radiation exposure, such as X rays, and atomic and nuclear energies. If our procedure is used before complete infection or inflammation has developed, then surgery is not necessary.

Additionally, the oral intake of mineral or vegetable oil in cup dosages relieves infection pressure and reduces inflammation, thereby preventing the escape of toxic poisons to the system from a ruptured appendix. Using the North pole energies further reduces the problem, especially in eliminating the stoppage of the passage to the appendix. In our animal research the use of lubricating oil with magnetic energy was effective in more than 90 percent of our cases, allowing the trapped fluid to circulate back to the middle of the appendix, reducing pressure and eliminating danger of rupture.

ARTHRITIS

Animals as they grow old suffer from arthritis, as do many persons. Although there are not as many types and kinds of arthritis as there are cancers, there are still many types. Some types of arthritis are caused by the development and growth of small hairlike fibers of calcium that develop and form across the joints of the fingers, arms, legs, and many parts of the body. During the research conducted toward arresting this calcium development we discovered that slow dissolution of this calcium was noted when the North pole was used to the feet and limbs of the animal. We used the North pole of the N-1 biomagnet for 30 to 40 minutes twice a day. Results were shown by X rays taken before and after a series of exposures to the North pole magnetic energy. Many cases responded well.

Time and results: Again, this depends on the advancement of calcium buildup on or around the joints. If total fusing of the joints has taken place, then little or nothing can be done to dissolve this fixed and fused joint to a point where it can again be flexible. This is with our present research knowledge.

In the neura types of arthritis, inflamed joints and associated disorders, the North pole energy alleviates pain and reduces inflamed joints and segments of the animal's body suffering from these complaints. *Time:* the same as in the research to dissolve calcium given above. *Magnet used:* the N-1 type. *Time for noticeable improvements:* dependent on the severity of the research animal's condition. Many cases recovered from inflamed muscles and pain in a week to several weeks.

BLADDER

Comparing certain human and animal difficulties with the bladder, we find that man suffers far more weakness of the bladder than animals. Where there is no infection, or there is a slight infection, a weakened, sagging or stretched bladder, it will respond to the tightening and reducing effects of the North pole of the biomagnet. *Time:* 30 minutes or twice a day directly to the bladder. *Location:* approximately two inches below the navel has shown excellent results. Where the bladder has grown weak, yet not enlarged, and no infection is present, the South pole has shown remarkable improvements in the strengthening of the bladder. This application is the same as the method described above in the use of the North pole of the biomagnet. Here it is of vital importance that the biological effects of the two poles of the biomagnet be properly understood.

BLEEDING/HEMORRHAGE

Many female animals suffer excessive bleeding and/or hemorrhaging during menstruation, before or after giving birth, or as a result of the weakness of certain organs. The application of the NORTH pole side of the biomagnet to the seat of the animal has shown effective relief in arresting the bleeding. This also applies to excessive fluid drainage from the rectum or female openings of the animal in question. Having the animal sit on the North pole of the biomagnet for 30 to 40 minutes twice a day, morning and evening, has proven effective arrest of many of these conditions in days or weeks, depending on the condition of the complaint.

Wounds, cuts, or bruises that fail to stop bleeding due to weak tissues have shown remarkable improvement and arrest by the use of the North pole energies. In regard to wounds and bleeding, we know that, during the latter part of World War II, Russian medical scientists used biomagnetics to aid healing and control of bleeding in cases of men wounded in the defense of their country. As we pointed out earlier, many nations of the world have been investigating and researching biomagnetics as a valuable new science; not only in the field of medical research, but also in its application to chemistry, protein advancement, healing wounds, and extending to the physics of new weapons systems that are classified in the areas of electronics and biochemistry.

BLOOD CLOTS

Reaction has been favorable to application of North pole energies as near as possible to the area externally on the skin's surface. With blood clots in legs and inner trunk arteries, the North pole applied to the exact location has shown the ability to SLOWLY reduce the clot fixed to inner arterial walls. *Time:* two 30-minute applications of 1800 to 3500 gauss magnet to the area once or twice a day; repeat only under careful supervision. This slow action serves an important function. The SLOW dissolution allows the body's natural abilities to assimilate the dissolution, thus preventing the clot from moving through the arteries to lodge in a major heart valve or supply system.

The North pole energies will hold, draw, and contain a deposit of water or blood fluids. Thus the clot is held in its location while dissolving in a manner not too rapidly.

In brain research the SLOW dissolving of clots, growths, and tumors is an important achievement in holding while dissolving biological growths and fluid masses with the North pole energies.

The N-1 biomagnet we have described varies in its strength applied in direct proportion to its distance from the difficulty. For example, if the blood clot is near the surface of the skin, it would receive the full strength of the magnet's 3500 gauss. If the clot or tumor was deeper, less than 3500 gauss would reach the area. The number of applications may be extended due to the location of the condition within the body system.

BLOOD PRESSURE

In animals as in man, there are a number of causes for high blood pressure. Eating excessive fatty foods acts to build fatty masses in and on the inner walls of the veins and arteries, limiting blood flow and increasing the blood pressure. Nervous conditions and congestion of arteries are other causes. The main cause, we believe, is the fatty buildup on the inner walls of the arteries.

Considerable research has been conducted in this field, because your senior author has fought this condition for many years. It was discovered that placing the NORTH pole of the N-1 biomagnet under the right ear, down the artery in that area, reduced the fatty buildup, and continued use reduced the blood pressure. For low blood pressure, the South pole energies are used. However, caution must be exercised not to bring the South pole energies near the brain.

Location: under the right ear against the artery that extends down the throat. *Time:* 30 minutes twice a day, morning and evening.

Continued use may be required, depending upon the condition, but usually there is a noticeable response on the first day of application.

BODY FLUIDS

Attraction and disbursement of biological body fluids can be accomplished with the energies of the N-1 biomagnet.

Application for 30 minutes to an area where water has collected under the skin or tissue of both large and small animals increases the activity of the fluids. The North pole energies draw fluids to its location. This occurs within 24 hours after application. On hundreds of research cases we placed the North pole 4 inches above or below the swelling or enlargement for 30 minutes; within 24 hours the water or fluids had been attracted to the exact location of application. This was further confirmed by placing the magnet 4 or 5 inches higher or lower the next day, the water and fluids again were attracted to the magnet's location.

In many experiments we have continued moving the magnet–the North pole energies–until the water or fluids have been accepted by the organs of the body. This dispelled, absorbed, and removed the excess fluids from the problem location. Excess fluids in the lungs have been brought down and to the back of animals in the lower lung areas.

Tapping is used in many hospitals to remove water deposits. However, this has proved unsuccessful in lower lung areas where the water is finely divided in the tissue. Continued placement of the North pole energies every 8 hours has collected the fluids where tapping may be employed or where the fluids may be removed by the natural functions of the body system.

The South pole energies are used when the fluids need to be dispersed. Placing the South pole directly on the location scatters the fluids throughout the body system. This energy application is not to be used with fluids that are better eliminated from the body system.

BONES/JOINTS

In the United States and other countries research is underway to heal weak bones and aid bone regrowth by inserting needles connected to a power supply similar to a flashlight battery. Biomagnetics has demonstrated a more desirable effect. No needles or batteries are required.

Pain can be reduced or totally arrested by application of the North pole energies to a sprain 30 minutes to one hour once or twice a day. Stronger healing results by applying the South pole above the location, with the North pole of another magnet applied below or on the location of the sprain.

BROKEN BONES AND FRACTURES

The South pole energies are always placed above

the break with the North pole energies of another magnet at the location of the bone that has been broken, with the North pole energies placed away from the undamaged part of the bone. This is an extended time of application again depending on the condition.

The South pole is a form of positive energy, while the North pole is a form of negative energy. The accepted law of all voltage and current is that positive energy flows from the South pole (positive) to the North pole (negative). Upon the initial start of this flow of energy a reverse energy flow occurs from the negative to the positive pole. This completes the two-way flow of energy occurring that we find applicable to voltage and currents, magnetism, and electromagnets. Our earlier book, *Magnetism and Its Effects on the Living System,* goes into detail on this function of magnetic energy.

By placing the separate magnets as indicated we establish a magnetic flow of energy to the damaged area. This has shown in many research cases to aid in healing and regrowth of bones. The natural energies of the body are increased at this point. We establish what is known as a closed circuit that speeds the mending action of the fracture or break with the added strength of energy in a closed loop or circuit flow of energy.

In further research we have reversed the closed circuit process mentioned above. We placed the South pole against the splintered break and the North pole to the end above the bone. The North pole acted to pull fluids and calcium to the broken end, while the South pole on the surface of the undamaged bone assisted with the

North pole closed loop to attract dissolved calcium particles across the break. This aided in removing fragmented particles of bone in a serious break, making them available in healing and regrowth. This latter method we have repeated in our research on older animals with serious breaks where it would generally be expected that bone healing would not function very effectively. Our results were satisfactory in over 90 percent of cases.

BRAIN RESEARCH

Tumor growth in the brain area is suffered by animals as well as man. Our research, although limited in this area, has produced significant discoveries. Here we use a round cylinder type magnet of 1200 to 1800 gauss about ½ inch in diameter directed to the area of the growth. *Time:* For 30 minutes twice to three times daily has acted to reduce, dissolve, and arrest the tumor. Number of treatments depends upon the condition. One day of treatment produces beneficial results. The cylinder magnet is used to avoid radiation to surrounding areas of the brain by concentration of energy to the desired location. Gauss strength is also reduced to lower amount with brain research. NORTH pole energies ONLY.

Although we have not used this method on blood clots in the brain, it would appear that further research would affirm this method of value in dissolving and removing the inactive blood to areas where it could be absorbed or more easily eliminated.

Inflamed membrane is a generic term concerning many serious conditions in this body area. The application of the NORTH pole energies, cylinder magnet, 1200 to 1800 gauss, to the surface area of the skull, has acted to reduce this inflamed condition. We have here the effect on water and fluids, described in the section on Body Fluids, removing brain pressure.

In large or small animals, including willing human subjects, the NORTH pole energies remove pressure, inflammation, and infection. They have improved the ability to walk, stand, think, and reason, depending on the condition of the inflammation.

Water on the brain or inner skull is another condition our research has covered in this area with limited subjects. This encompasses our research with fluids, including blood and plasma. Where water, blood, or fluids exist in an unbalanced amount the NORTH pole energies ONLY will draw these materials to the location where the magnet is placed. Our section on Body Fluids should be included in study with this application.

The NORTH pole energies will reduce inflamed conditions, relieve pressure from swollen, infected, or inflamed membrane coverings, and arrest and dissolve growths pressing on the brain. This can occur between the skull and the brain's insulating materials or between the membrane coating and the insulation mass of protective materials. For fluid problems the cylinder magnet, 1200 to 1800 gauss, is better placed about 2 to 3 inches from the problem area 30 minutes once or twice a day, the NORTH pole ONLY. Within 24 hours the fluid will be drawn to the location where the magnet was placed. This process is repeated every 24 hours. The fluids are drawn to an area in a dissolved nature to enter the arteries and large veins that will dissipate the fluids. This eliminates the necessity of opening the brain's covering by drilling and removing part of the skull. It is interesting to note that surgery of this nature performed today was the practice over a thousand years ago.

We hope this research approach of magnetic energy will be a definite improvement for animals, including man, instead of the primitive method now used in drilling, sawing, and opening of the skull. Because Biomagnetics is not properly investigated and understood by the great majority of scientists and medical men today, it may be many years before this new discovery development is enacted for beneficial use. The adoption of this science will come when more of our research is duplicated by scientists and medical men. The knowledge of this science, its applications and significance, will progress more rapidly when more persons of all endeavors are familiar with the computer-exact results of these discoveries.

BRONCHITIS

Generally, bronchitis is an acute infection of the air passages starting at the nose and into the lungs. This is an INFECTION; therefore, we must remember that the North pole is the arrester and the South pole is the strength-giving or affecting pole. In this case of research we would use the North pole because this is an INFECTION. Placing the North pole of the biomagnet against the nose, then throat, then lungs, for 8 minutes at each location, has shown a marked arrest of this condition. Time for noticeable improvements depends on the health and strength of the subject, and the degree that the complaint has been allowed to develop.

BURNS

Local or limited area burns: Apply the North pole directly to the burn area for 30 to 45 minutes 2 or 3 times a day to limit or arrest pain from burns. The healing is best after pain has been arrested by continued use of the North pole. After scab has formed over the burn there is NO INFECTION. Application of the South pole should then be started for strength to aid the new tissue to form over the burn. For large area burns, slowly apply the research outlined above until the total area has been covered. This research has shown new and greater approaches to aid man and child alike; women react slightly slower to recovery. This also applies to the animals we have worked with in our research. Results have been outstanding and very rewarding in this work.

CANCER AND CANCER TUMORS

Primary to advanced types of 1, 2, 3, 4, A, B, C, D classifications have been arrested by the application of the North pole energies with 1800 to 3500 gauss strength.

In the arrest of transplanted cancers, and in later research with advanced skin cancers, the time was 45 minutes, 3 times a day for 3 weeks. After the first week of application noticeable reduction in the size of the cancer area was recorded. Because no two animals will react in the exact same manner, time varied for total arrest reaction by exposure of the animal's cancer to the North pole of the N-1 biomagnet. On a general average, the time of 3 months showed all signs of cancer arrested and removed. In many cases less time was effective.

The research we have conducted in cancers and cancer tumors covers many years, and many rewarding discoveries have resulted. This is all by the study and application of magnetic fields. During these years of research we have had visitors from many nations of the world, doctors and M.D.'s and scientists in many fields of research, all interested in our research and findings. The Russians are, and have been, investigating magnetic effects on living system also. We spoke of this in the section of this research report dealing with bleeding control, pain, and wound arrest and healing.

The Russian scientists have also been investigating the research of cancer arrest and control by magnetic energy, biomagnetics. So are Japan, Germany, and England. Some research has been done by certain men and women scientists here in certain colleges and universities and in a few limited laboratories. The great difficulty we have technically is to convince all researchers of our discovery that the two poles of a magnet are *not* homogeneous (the same) in nature of their electronic potential, or the effects on the living system. Russia has followed the same incorrect theories that are used in this country and in other countries of the world today. Books written on the magnet in biological research state that there is no difference between the North or the South poles of a magnet.

We feel that we may have been the first scientists to introduce biomagnetic living system research showing the two effects, or the effects of each separate pole of the magnet. This we introduced to the doctors and scientists in many parts of India, later South America and other nations, including a number of American doctors and scientists.

We would like at this time to disclose that Russian scientists may soon announce a cancer detection system using a super type of biomagnet, high-powered and concentrated fields, directly to the human system. We also believe that when this announcement is made, and it may be made before this book is completed, they will not have discovered the great effects and differences between the two separate poles of the biomagnet's potentials in applying their powerful super magnet for this work.

What Is a Cancer?

The common cancer is the result of a single cell breaking down and decomposing. Discussing this in a nontechnical manner, when we view a red blood cell, we see through a very high-powered electron microscope a doughnut-shaped round cell that has a recess in its center like a doughnut. It is when the outer walls of the cell break down, and these outer walls are called the membrane, that fluid flows from the cell that under normal conditions would be retained within the cell itself. The membrane or covering of the cell's fluids is much the same as a filter. It allows through it certain fluids of the body and prevents others from entering the cell. When this selectivity lessens in one cell alone, there is the start of a condition of cancer, because this one cell then can transmit this electrolyte, this unbalanced electrolyte fluid, to the walls of other cells. This acts to transfer actively to the next, and so on, unselectively. When the selectivity of the membrane is made unselective, then the cell allows, into and out of it, chemicals that act to destroy its electrical balances. This acts to cause the cell to decompose and rot away. This simple term *rot* we feel well explains a cancer, as those of us know who have seen a skin cancer and have noted the odor and a fluid-filled, pussy discharge hole in the skin.

Although skin cancer can be considered to be the least of all cancers, it offers the layman a chance to see with his or her eyes the actual results of this condition.

Science is seeking a way to control the characteristic rapid and uncontrolled multiplications of cancer cells. The negative energies transmitted from the North pole of a magnet may be the answer to this problem. We have shown in our research that the growth and multiplication of cancer cells can be arrested and eliminated by negative magnetic energy.

DIGESTION AND STOMACH GAS

In research on animals in arresting problems of poor digestion, we have found few specimens for our work. Animals, unlike man, can more easily expel indigestible or tainted food from the mouth. It is not so much that man cannot do this as that man is not accustomed to react in this manner. Man is also not so aware as the animals that dizziness or a sick stomach are telling him of this problem.

Gas on the stomach is usually the result of poor digestion or too much acid in the stomach. Then man turns to antacid tablets and powders to neutralize the gas.

Applying the South pole of the N-1 biomagnet to the stomach 20 to 30 minutes once or twice a day has shown improvement in arresting poor digestion and stomach gas.

Laboratory research shows the South pole energies upgrade natural acids for more effectiveness. Even though the body system produces forms of bicarbonates to control acids in the stomach, the system can fail to produce sufficiently to control high amounts effectively.

We have given the presently accepted opinions on indigestion, but we disagree with the accepted medical and clinical reasoning in this matter. Our findings are based on actual research and are not to promote the sale of acid powders, tablets, or other temporary reliefs as advertised.

In large and small animal research, and in limited willing human subjects, we have found that *lack* of acids, not excess of acids, in the stomach, could be the cause for stomach gas, upset stomach, and indigestion. Our laboratory findings demonstrate a lack of digestive acids, not the over-amounts, to be the cause of these problems. When antacid tablets and powders are taken internally they neutralize acids in the stomach that are already in amounts too low.

Without hydrochloric acid levels at a good amount food cannot be digested. Their fermentation of the food produces gas and indigestion. The unnatural intake of antacid materials neutralizes natural digestive acids. Although the cause is incorrectly described, the result is effective. The antacid materials open the acid-forming ducts in the stomach's generating supply system, thus flooding the stomach with a greater amount of natural acids. These natural acids go to work digesting and passing the food by-products to the lower digestive system.

We note that antacid materials, of whatever kind, make or manufacture, without water intake, must be of a strength that will upset the person's feelings, senses and well-being, because too high a reaction taste occurs in the mouth and throat areas as well as the stomach. Water should always be taken with these antacids to aid chemical dilution. This is also true of aspirin. Water is required for intake. With too little water to aid in the breakup of such chemicals, heartburn and more stomach indigestion can occur. This is caused by the lack of natural acids, not the excess of acids as is commonly advertised. In research we seek the cause as well as the effects. A scientist should know why a condition occurs as well as how to apply countermeasures to correct the condition. Application of the South pole energies increases the natural acid exchange in the stomach, thus relieving these stomach conditions.

EAR RESEARCH

Animals suffer the same complaints as man with infections, weak audio nerves, and poor hearing.

The outcome of many research cases in this area has shown that the NORTH pole of a N-1 biomagnet placed against the swelling of the outer ear, which may be caused by infection, will reduce the problem in a few weeks or less. Time is 30 minutes twice a day, the number of days depending on the nature and type of complaint.

Swelling of the flesh around the ear may be due to infection of the innermost parts of the ear, yet not the inner ear. There may be a hardened condition in the ear's diaphragm. This part of the ear acts to transmit sound waves and air pressures into vibrations that are received by the inner ear's audio nerves. The South pole application for this cause has shown to be valuable in aiding the ear diaphragm to be flexible again. The hearing is thus improved. Time is as indicated above.

Remember, the NORTH pole is used for infection, NOT the South pole.

Ear drainage problems result in infection of the inner ear. This is one of the most difficult ear complaints to arrest. The NORTH pole, as for ANY INFECTION, is used 30 minutes morning and evening hours in the proper method. Time is about 4 to 8 weeks depending on the degree of infection.

Earache is usually due to a cold of the ear. This may be considered a form of infection. NORTH pole energies 20 to 25 minutes twice a day should relieve the ache in a day or two. More applications are used if condition is advanced.

EMOTIONS

In the study of animal behavior we find similarities between animal and man. Both show identical reactions to their environmental surroundings. Love and kindness are the basis of harmony, understanding, and resultant behavior.

A spoiled, overdemanding pet is the result of lax discipline and training. Overcritical treatment will also destroy a pleasant relationship between the animal and man.

An overcritical or lax attitude of a human to an animal is a reflection of that human's inner makeup. The animal, like the human child, can sense these inner emotional conflicts. Inferiority or persecution complexes, overaggressiveness, irrational behavior of the human will develop a state of uncertain behavior in the animal. The animal may live in fear of the human.

Emotional problems, as in humans, can become complicated in animal behavior. It is difficult to determine the specific cause and condition for the particular energy application.

Basically, if the animal is overaggressive, seating the animal on the North pole of the N-1 biomagnet, with care and patience, will result in a slow yet definite change to calmness. Short periods of time each day should bring noticeable change the first week.

If the animal is slow, dull, inactive, then seating the animal on the South pole of the N-1 biomagnet for short periods of time as indicated above will result in a more energetic animal.

In application of the energy for emotions, extreme care is necessary to establish that no physical problem exists for the behavior, because a particular physical problem could be aggravated by the energy application. Short, infrequent applications are desired to determine results. If results are not as expected a physical cause should be investigated.

EYES AND CATARACTS

The eyes of animals and man are similar in the conditions they suffer. Cataracts can develop on the animal's eyes as they do on man's eyes. The use of the NORTH pole on the affected eye, or eyes, for 12 minutes a day, morning and evening hours, has shown that a number of types of cataracts can be arrested and contained. In a number of research cases, the cataract appeared to leave the eyes with no side effects noted. If this was a dissolving of this foreign growth (cataract) then this research result indicates the continuance of the effects of the North pole of the biomagnet to arrest and assist in the removal of foreign matter deposits from the segments of the living system. Over 60 percent of the cases researched have shown improvements; over 20 percent have shown total recovery of the condition.

FEMALE REPRODUCTIVE ORGANS

In practical and actual research, it has been our findings that both the male and the female animal can develop many weaknesses that limit or stop altogether the normal desire for sex. In females this can produce a marked retirement from life as they know and understand it. They become unhappy, tired, retiring, nerves acting at times to make them angry. The kindness and normal behavior of the female's life is greatly affected. The application of the biomagnet to the seat of the female will strengthen the sexual reproductive organs, uplift the nerve responses, and give back, totally or partially, that condition needed by the female system. The seating of the female on the South pole side of the biomagnet for 30 minutes before going to bed each night acts to encourage strength and aid in the return to a more nearly normal behavior pattern.

FEMALE BLEEDING/EXCESSIVE FLUID DRAINAGE

In this phase of our research we have found that the control effects of the NORTH pole of the magnet act to reduce bleeding and excessive fluid drainage. The act of sitting on the North pole of the biomagnet for 30 minutes, or in advanced cases applying it to the seat for 30 minutes in morning and evening hours, acts in a short time to arrest this excessive or limited bleeding and/or fluids that drain or come from the female openings.

FEMALES UNABLE TO DEVELOP BABIES

If infertility is caused by weakness, and miscarriage continues, the female animals may be seated on the SOUTH pole of the biomagnet for 30 minutes twice a day, morning and evening hours. This acts to strengthen the muscles and tissues to enable the female to carry the young. As soon as the young is seen to be in good development, this research can be discontinued. Continued use of the South pole to the seat would then, as we have found in a number of research cases, produce larger babies. This would cause difficulty in delivery due to its size or development.

GLAUCOMA

Glaucoma is the hardening of the eyes as a result of internal pressure caused by trapped fluids. One or more of the passages that provide circulating fluids into and out of the eyes may have closed. This is due to a buildup of foreign materials on the inner walls of the passages or a vessel of the passage system. The presence of swelling or of foreign material in one or both of the fluid passages to the eyes can cause glaucoma. Because approximately 90 percent of the eye is composed of sodium chloride (salt), the hardening causes great pain and suffering. Although there are a number of types of glaucoma, we will give the results of those types that we have been able to research. By applying the North pole field to the outer edges of each eye that is to be researched with biomagnetics, for 15 minutes twice a day, we have noted a reduction of pain and pressure expressed as "hardness of the eye." We feel strongly that this indicator will show us still additional uses for the control effects presented by the NORTH pole of the biomagnet to this condition.

HAIR COLORING

Many researchers have asked whether or not the application of biomagnetics could improve the hair coloring of animal or man. In this phase of research we have found that it does in a limited number of cases. Of course, this depends on the health of the animal or man. A rundown condition of an animal will not present any improvements to hair coloring; this would also apply to man. The greatest strength-giving factor we have found is to place the seat of the animal on the South pole of the biomagnet for 20 to 30 minutes each night after it has gone to bed. This we have found acts to strengthen the animal's entire system in general. Some coloring of the hair back to a more natural color and improved texture has been noted.

HEADACHES AND NEURALGIA

Man suffers from headaches and neuralgia more than animals do. Causes we have found for this condition include limited bowel action, weak liver, overeating, poor digestion, overwork, and nerve reaction to strain, worry, and fear.

Normal bowel movements of the animal do not remove all of the toxins from the system. As the animal system grows older this is more evident. The liver, as well as the kidneys, are instrumental in the control of these poisons.

Placing the South pole against the lower stomach produces marked improvement in assisting the removal of digested foods and upgrading the strength of other basic organs, relieving some headaches and neuralgia.

The cause for these complaints should be determined. Then the application as described in the specific section of this book can be researched. The intake of foods such as vegetables and fruits is helpful.

HEART

In researching the effects of biomagnetism on the heart, we are again faced with many possible causes and complaints. For the protection of the animal, the specific complaint must be determined before undertaking any research application.

Animals, like man, develop weak hearts. The muscles of the heart will weaken, resulting in murmurs. The pulse rate of the heartbeat may decrease in speed. Applying the SOUTH pole of the N-1 biomagnet over the heart for 10 minutes twice a day, morning and evening, shows a marked increase in strength. The beat of the heart becomes stronger. Weakened valves and muscles in and near the heart have also responded to this application.

Emergency heart stimulation has saved many animals in our research. We have had animals where the pulse rate dropped to 25 to 40 beats per minute, fluttering, pause and beat action occurring. This has happened in small to large animals. Many were tested after an accident or minor to major surgery. Surgical shock will take the lives of animals as it does the lives of men, women, and children.

Heart-stimulating drugs and open chest massage are common methods for beat failure on the operating table. Electrical shock treatments are increasing in use. These methods all have their limitations. Where the heart rate has dropped very low, with fluttering, pause or stop, the application of the SOUTH pole of the N-1 biomagnet is helpful. Location is slightly above the middle of the shoulder blades about 10 to 12 inches below the base of the neck. There is an immediate reaction. In 10 minutes the heart action will strengthen with a beat of 78 to 84 per minute. The smaller the animal the faster return of strength, versus a slow return for the larger animal, generally. In willing human subjects the above strength return was noted. In medium-size animals the average normal heartbeat may be as much as 125 per minute. Smaller animals average as high as 150 heartbeats per minute. It is interesting to ponder that larger animals have a slower heartbeat, and the larger the animal the longer it lives.

Further prevention of operation shock into cardio arrest can be helped by placing the South pole as indicated for 5 to 10 minutes BEFORE the operation. This strengthens the heart. Also, in applying for 5 minutes, removing for 10 minutes, applying 5 minutes, again removing, before and during the operation. After an operation or shock condition, the application of the South pole as indicated for 30 minutes has shown positive stimulation to the heart's strength.

IMPORTANT to remember that removal of the magnet must be SLOW. Remove after each application slowly, a little distance at a time, several feet from the body area. Time of removal about 30 seconds. Otherwise, a fast removal could result in shock to the heart.

Slowing the heart pace is possible if desired. Care and caution are advisable with the North pole application, same location. If the pace drops too low, then change the application to South pole energy to restore normal pulse rate.

A horseshoe magnet may be used on emergency if a bar magnet is not available. Place the South and North poles to the location. Time will be longer but the heart pace will improve and strengthen.

INFECTION/STRENGTH

When the condition of infection is found and research is desired to be undertaken with biomagnetics, the NORTH POLE is the arresting pole. The North pole DOES NOT KILL THE INFECTION OR BACTERIA. It does arrest the further development of the infection in many cases, depending on the nature of the infection. When we use the word *arrest* or *arresting* we mean that the further development of the infection is controlled. When any form of infection is arrested the body's own chemical system can then take over and begin a slow state of recovery, because NO form of treatment of any kind can repair the damage from such forms of biological damage to the body. The body itself does the healing and makes its own repairs. Time varies with condition.

INFECTION/CONGESTION

Let us properly define the two conditions and their general meanings: an *infection* is a condition where there is bacteria, germs, pus, inflamed and running sores. Internal infection may be found where there is a serious disease. *Congestion* is the blockage or reduction of a passageway. A vessel may be closed or nearly closed. Lungs may be filled with foreign materials, thereby causing a state of congestion, but no infection may be present. A swelling that affects the passages preventing expelling of air may be called congestion. Proper application is the South pole as described in the section on lung congestion. You MUST rule out infection because the South pole would increase any infection that is present.

KIDNEY RESEARCH

An animal, like man, can and does at times develop diseased or poorly operating kidneys. Pain and swelling of the lower right or left back surface indicates this in a number of cases, or where the urine is very dark and containing pus. Then there is that possibility of the formation and development of kidney stones. Because of the chemical compositions of most animals, however, this does not happen too often. Man experiences this more than any of nature's animals. In human animals this is caused in most cases by the high calciums and foreign matter in drinking water.

In researching the control of pain of the affected kidneys, as well as the reduction of the inflamed condition or minor infections, where biomagnetics has been used in this form of research the results have been both outstanding and rewarding. The approach is to place the NORTH pole of the biomagnet directly against the kidney location for 40 minutes to an hour once or twice a day, morning and evening hours best. In a very short time, pain, swelling, and pus discharge have been reduced; there is also a clearer urine color. More time or less time may be needed, depending on the case in question.

It is of great interest to note that a number of so called inoperative kidneys, partially dead, have been restored to a limited amount of production after the application of the North pole magnetic fields. We strongly feel that this research discovery may lead someday to the use of biomagnetics to aid in the control or arrest of complaints now most difficult to cope with by the medical profession. This should prove an important step forward in kidney research.

LIVER RESEARCH

In liver research it is all but impossible to note the advanced cases of liver ailments in animals, except by the yellowish color of the eyes, and yellow to pale green coloring of the facial skin, where normal pink coloring should be noted. However, when this condition has been found to exist, and biomagnetic research has been applied, a very good number of recoveries has been noted. In infection of the liver, and the failure of its operations, the cause must be known, if we are to approach this type of research properly, effectively, and correctly. If there is a failure of the liver, by infection or a disease, then from all past research results, the NORTH pole, the arresting pole, should be applied to the general location of the liver for 30 to 45 minutes 3 times a day. We have found that twice a day may prove to be effective in some simple to not far advanced cases. As soon as tests show, or coloring is noted, an improvement back to a normal healthy skin or clearing eyes, the time should be reduced to 30 minutes morning and evening. When all signs or tests indicate the liver is working normally, then discontinue the research applications. We may find that only a part of the diseased liver is left intact, but if there is enough of this organ left to do the job, we consider this to be an effective arrest and accept it as another successful project undertaking.

LUNGS/COLDS AND CONGESTION

The common cold is the mystery of the ages. Animals suffer from colds, as does all mankind. The end results are inflamed passages that limit breathing, or present a flow of fluids from the nose. Inflamed inner air passages of the nose and lungs and throat soreness can result from the common cold. Our research in this area was undertaken only when we saw the suffering of the animals and compared it with man's colds. We then placed the North pole to the region of the nose, then the throat, then the lungs for 7 to 8 minutes at each location. The flat surface of the North pole of the biomagnet directly against those areas did, in many cases, aid and arrest the discomfort of the colds. Here we do have a form of bacteria. In cases of CONGESTION ONLY, SOUTH POLE.

The lungs: Because the lungs may suffer many types of ailments, diseases, and complaints, no one use or method of application of biomagnetic energy may result in any form of relief; it is necessary to know beforehand the nature of the complaint. If the lungs are congested, with NO infection present, then the application of the SOUTH pole of the biomagnet directly to the lungs will act to expand, open, and relieve the congestion and breathing. The lesson of what the South pole's energy does is hereby noted, as the strength-giving or affecting pole; the North pole is the reducing, the arresting pole.

MUSCLES

Our section on sprains is helpful reading on the subject of muscles.

For weak muscles the NORTH pole biomagnet will aid in firming. Then the application of the South pole acts to strengthen. Time is 20 to 30 minutes a day of North pole. After noticeable firming of muscles change to the South pole application, time the same, until suitable strength occurs.

PANCREAS RESEARCH

The accepted theories today are in accord for the condition of a sugar diabetic where the production of sugar-burning insulin fails to be in the amounts needed to burn, use, and consume the sugars produced by the intake of food, or the sugars produced by the animal's body. The pancreas, according to accepted principal theories, develops an inability to produce this insulin in sufficient amounts to use the sugars produced. In the application of biomagnets to a limited number of cases, it was found that applying the South pole of the biomagnet to the general area of the pancreas for 30 minutes, morning and evening hours, appeared to have either raised the amount of insulin produced by the pancreas or strengthened it to a point where fewer positive blood sugars were noted. If this application overactivates the liver, then apply the South pole to the midback for energy to the pancreas.

Samples were taken and tested for sugars in the urine after applications of North or South pole energies. Here, again, we note that the effects of the SOUTH pole of the applied biomagnet afford strength to an organ, a part, or a segment of the living system. In the research on overproductive pancreas activities the NORTH pole has arrested a limited number of research cases.

PARATHYROID GLANDS/CONTROL OF CALCIUMS

Research shows that SWELLING of these four small glands can be reduced and arrested by biomagnetic energy exposures. The research is the same as that described for the thyroid glands. Place the North pole of the biomagnet against the sides of the neck, time the same as in the thyroid section. The parathyroid glands act to control an even amount of calcium in the blood.

We have found that when calciums are not properly controlled, arthritis can be a result. With no infection present in the thyroids, the South pole of the biomagnet can be applied to the sides of the neck for 15 minutes each day. This we have found, by direct research, can stimulate the calciums and improve the blood. THE NORTH POLE REDUCES the calciums, or levels the production of calciums in joints and fingers, which in many cases cause many types of arthritis. This does not apply to all cases. A limited number have, however, shown positive results. These small glands also act to control the amounts of calcium in the blood. It would appear that should we apply the South pole of the biomagnet to these glands, we could affect a rise in the calciums in the blood. When this may be needed it is worthy research.

Caution: Never apply the South pole to any location on a living system where there is a swelling or an inflamed condition or infection is present. THE NORTH POLE REDUCES, while the SOUTH POLE INCREASES.

PILES/HEMORRHOIDS

In general, piles are brought about by the weakness of blood vessels and arteries located at the near bottom of the seat, or opening, of the bowels. Extending of this condition prompts bleeding, pain, and discomfort. This is caused by a general weakness of the system.

Sitting on the North pole of the biomagnet 30 to 45

minutes three times a day, or twice a day, will aid in the reduction of the condition as well as pain and discomfort. AFTER pain and discomfort have been reduced, THEN, the application of the South pole biomagnet will aid in restoring strength of the body condition. South pole only once or twice a day. Night hours, when the subject is at rest, are the best time for this South pole application. Use South pole for 30 to 45 minutes each application. The South pole will strengthen the vessels and arteries by a process of lifting up and backing into the body. Some form of lubrication should also be applied to aid relief.

The cause of why this complaint occurs should be attended to or the complaint will occur again and again. The animal system is overplaying, lacking rest, not having the proper nourishing foods. Corrections should be undertaken to prevent recurrences.

PROSTATE AND THE MALE ANIMAL

The male animal, like the human male, suffers from the complaints or inactivity of the prostate glands. Sex is a drive that gives all animal forms a desire to live and to get things accomplished. When trouble strikes this gland, the sex life is reduced, and the animal's life is affected. The production of fluids by the prostate gland can be increased by having the animal sit on the South pole of the magnet for 30 minutes, once each night, after it has gone to its bed. Place the animal's seat directly on the South pole of the biomagnet 30 minutes each night, or in more difficult research cases twice a day, morning and evening hours. Improvements should be noticed at once, or in a few days at most, unless the condition is very advanced. Then more time will be needed, but, under normal conditions, results have been recorded in a matter of days.

Watch the animal. A marked improvement of interest in things, and playing or working with new interests in its pattern of behavior, indicates that the research exposures are working. Research can be slowed or ended, and the animal watched for any decline; if a decline occurs again, and a lack of interest is noted, then return to the research treatment as described. Each case being different in nature, it will take study to see when the animal returns to normal. When this happens the research exposure to the biomagnetic South pole can be discontinued. Prolonged use may lead to an excessive desire for sex.

When the male animal is seated on the South pole of the biomagnet the testicles will also receive amounts of this stimulating magnetic energy. This may cause a rise in desire for sex. The amount of fluids produced by the prostate have been laboratory measured against untreated animals, and after several days of exposure, the amount of the prostatic fluid is increased by a good percentage.

REST PERIODS

The biological clock of animal and man needs adjustment to energy system corrections.

If applications of biomagnetic energy are necessary for periods of time longer than one week, there should be a rest period.

One day a week should be free of any biomagnet application. We chose Saturday or Sunday in our research. The day is optional. This allows the system to adjust naturally to the effects applied. This is necessary in extended treatment. One day a week is for rest. NO application allowed.

SEX LIFE AND AGING

Animals, including man, experience the same difficulties with the series of life cycle events called sex life and aging. Difficulties, as such, deal directly with the beginning stages of life, and the growing knowledge of the world and its environment.

With animals their environment is the home, the persons in that home, the attention received, the presence or lack of love received. These factors go into the molding of the animal's personality. All animals, like men, women and children, have personalities. In this sense all animals are totally different, one from the other. This applies to all species, types, and kinds of animals.

We find that the sex life of all animals governs the rate of aging. As with men and women, if sex is denied the animal, it can become without drive, desire, interest, love, or kindness. On the other hand, oversex results in premature aging, weakness, and lack of healthy interests. There should be some form of natural balance to even out the desire or lack of desire. Our findings are general in this regard. They do not deny exceptions.

Unlike men and women, animals have two natural cycles of sex, well-defined to the physical and mental desires of the animals. These cycles occur in the spring and fall.

In the research on magnetism applied to all forms of life systems, placing the animal's seat on the North pole reduces the desire for sex. Opposed to this, placing the South pole to the seat acts to promote the desire for sex. These results occur in disregard of the natural sex cycle.

Time for this research is 20 minutes morning and evening. A sensible manner of restraining an animal for this application may be necessary to prevent injury while in restraint.

The N-1 biomagnet may be used. Magnets of less strength, from 800 to 1500 gauss, have been found satisfactory for this research. Be sure your research magnets are correctly identified, North pole and South pole. We emphasize that the North pole of a magnet seeks a South pole attraction; the South pole, a North pole attraction. Identify the poles correctly.

SHOULDERS/NEURITIS

Neuritis is a condition of nerve inflammation. Where this condition is evident, the North pole of the N-1 biomagnet is used. Application is the flat surface of the North pole directly to the painful area 30 to 45 minutes, morning and evening. This will reduce the inflamed condition and accompanying pain. The number of applications depends upon how far the condition has advanced.

SINUS/SINUSES

Small magnets no larger than a silver dollar are best for sinus research.

The cavities in the skull above and below the eyes build up fluid pressure and pain. Swelling and blockage occurs in the openings leading from the sinus cavities.

DO NOT use the N-1 biomagnet for this research. Small magnets, as described, are required. The North pole negative energies relieve pain, fluid pressure, and the swelling and blockage.

Time is 15 minutes above and below the eye of the affected side. In severe cases, ONLY 7 minutes twice a day to each affected cavity. The number of required applications varies with seriousness of condition, but the pain effect does not return as frequently.

SPINE CURVE

Spine curve is one of the most difficult conditions to correct. Muscles can become weak, sprained or pulled. The spine responds in a curve, a pull to one side or the other.

Many D.C.'s correct spine curves by bone adjustment, yet in many cases this alignment will return. Muscles are semifixed. They retain a pull that renders correction difficult. Our animal research in this area involved two different methods of application. One method uses one magnet; the other method, two magnets.

In the two-magnet method, we place an N-1 biomagnet on each side of the curve or pull strain. The South pole was placed where the curve was more pronounced. The expanding effects of this energy aided to release the tightening muscles on that side of the curve. The North pole energy acted to pull the muscles to that direction. The North pole pulls; the South pole expands. Both magnets are applied at the same time. The North pole pulls the muscles, allowing more freedom for the spine to straighten, while the South pole expands the contracted muscles, allowing the North pole energies to pull with more flexibility. This interaction of energies has demonstrated positive correction with extended application in a number of research cases.

Time of application is 30 to 40 minutes twice a day, morning and evening hours, or one hour once a day. In a week to weeks, depending on condition, an improvement will be noticed in most cases. In animal research where animals have received a blow by a motor vehicle, this research has proved effective in straightening the spine in many cases.

One N-1 biomagnet may be used in this research. With this method, the South pole flat surface is FIRST placed against the side of the spine where the curve is more pronounced. Time is 30 minutes, then allowing 12 hours rest without application. After 12 hours have passed, apply the North side of the magnet to the opposite side. Time here is 30 minutes. The North pole is applied to the side that is curved inward. If this is accomplished once a day for a week to weeks, depending on condition, an improvement will be noticed.

Continuing either method of application will have a lasting effect in correction. Our research in this area involved hundreds of small to large animal cases.

SPRAINS

Sprained back and ankle, sprain of hip or leg muscles, sprain of shoulders, have all responded to the North pole application of the N-1 biomagnet. The North pole acts to reduce, contract, and lessen pain. This assists the recovery of the sprained condition.

This section is smiliar to our section on muscles. Apply North pole 20 to 30 minutes a day to firm up muscles; then, after noticeable firming of muscles, apply South pole 20 to 30 minutes a day for strength. The number of treatments always depends upon condition.

TEETH AND GUMS

Decaying teeth, infected gums, infected roots of teeth, swelling, pus deposits, pus sacks under teeth, soft gums, loose teeth in gums, have all responded well to the North pole energy.

Application is 30 to 40 minutes twice a day, morning and evening. The best time for application is after feeding the animal. The animal is less restless, allowing more ease in holding or bandaging the biomagnet to the location.

The number of applications will be determined by condition. Generally, pain is reduced in 3 to 4 applications. Loose teeth show a marked improvement in several weeks.

THROAT

Sore throat is a mild form of infection. North pole, directly to the front of the throat 20 minutes twice a day; in one or two days a noticeable improvement will be shown.

For weak throats, where no colds or infection are present, use the South pole against the throat 15 to 20 minutes twice a day, for a few days at most. As improvements are noted, continue with this research until best results are obtained.

THYROID GLAND

Research shows that swelling of the thyroid gland located on either side of the neck front can be arrested by North pole energy.

Apply the N-1 biomagnet to each side, 15 minutes to each, once a day. Advanced cases require morning and evening hours, 15 minutes to each side twice a day.

The thyroid gland is subject to many kinds of disorders. Investigation should be made to determine cause of swelling. The extended use of the North pole energy will reduce swelling in more advanced cases.

TUMORS

Tumors may form on any gland. Glands that present tumor development can develop into cancer. Our section on cancer and cancer tumors should be read with this section.

Tumors, not developed cancers, can be arrested and dissolved by North pole application of the N-1 biomagnet directly to the condition.

Time is 30 to 45 minutes twice a day. The results depend upon each case, the type and kind of tumor, and the condition of the tumor.

Tumors in the brain area are not researched with the N-1 biomagnet. Less gauss energy is effective. We used a round cylinder type of magnet 1200 to 1800 gauss energy. Refer to our section on brain research.

ULCERS

Ulcers, which occur frequently in man, are almost nonexistent in animals. But there are cases where they do develop.

Use of the North pole N-1 biomagnet to the stomach area of the ulcer furnishes the necessary energy for control and arrest.

Apply the North pole below the navel, or where the navel would be on the human body, for 30 to 40 minutes twice a day, morning and evening. Number of applications as desired for condition. Relief is noticeable after the first day of application in most cases.

In our research we have also found that ordinary water is helpful after the water has been subjected to the North pole energies. We apply the North pole energy to water 5 to 15 minutes, then allow the animal to drink. This research has extended to application of North pole energy to the milk that the animals drink. Place a container of milk on a nonmetal table; then place the N-1 biomagnet, or a cylinder 1200 to 1800 gauss magnet, against the bowl or glass for 15 to 20 minutes. Then allow the animal to drink the milk. All these methods were effective in our ulcer research with animals, including application of the North pole energy to their food. NOTE: Some animals, like human beings, cannot properly digest milk in their systems. We have found that treating milk with the North pole energy allows many of these animals to properly digest the milk. We are continuing research in this area.

VERTEBRAS

Where continued slipping occurs from location in the spine, the application of the North pole N-1 biomagnet aids in reducing the overplay, assisting to maintain a correct position.

North pole acts to pull, to contract muscles. Then the South pole can be used to strengthen the area. Time is 30 minutes twice a day. North pole is used for suitable contraction. After the muscles are in proper location only then should the South pole be used. Our sections on muscles and spine curves are helpful reading with this complaint.

CHAPTER V

AMPUTATED LIMB PARTIAL REGROWTH

In our research on regrowth processes in the reptile species of animals, the development of tissue, bones, nerve endings, and sensitivities to feelings has shown promising results.

If the energy of a magnet can alter the existing genetics of certain animals, would the possibility exist of replacing limbs, partially or totally, that have been severed or amputated?

Other medical researchers have advised that a human animal, upon removal and healing of an amputated limb, retains a sense of feeling that the limb is still present and intact. The nerve endings assist this sensibility.

Our first attempt in this research was to discover if the North or South pole of the magnet, taped against the stump of an amputated limb, would act in any way on the senses of the nerve endings.

With a number of willing human subjects we were able to determine that the North pole application rendered a sense of "no feeling" that the limb or extended member was present. We were advised by the subjects that this assisted to improve their state of mind concerning their condition.

This basic research was accomplished some 12 years ago. Many doctors and researchers showed interest in this discovery, yet we know of no medical research undertaken to apply this discovery. Medical staff members at the Veterans Hospital in Atlanta, Georgia, and in Washington, D.C., were informed. We had hoped that government research would investigate this discovery for further development. To our knowledge no attention was directed in furthering this research.

Our research involved the use of 1000 gauss magnetic tape, North pole 1/16 inch thick by 3 to 4 inches wide applied directly to the stump.

Because this discovery involving human subjects elicited no responsive action by authorities, we turned to further research in this area on the healing of animals. With the reptile species we discovered that the North pole energy would act to aid regrowth where an extended limb had been amputated.

Using the North pole energy, 800 to 1200 gauss, four hours on the stump and four hours off, then changed to two hours twice a day, the results were the same. Growth occurred from ¼ to ½ inch beyond the stump end.

When the South pole energy was applied, the scar tissue acted to expand, rather than grow to an oval ending. This expansion of tissue continued. Small extensions of flesh were noted after some 60 days of amputation in the small reptile group. There appeared new minute size extensions. This presented the recorded fact that the blastite genetics of the small reptile, which does not normally regenerate lost limbs, could be encouraged to develop partial regrowth of limbs. Claws started their reforming.

These earlier experiments in the use of the separate pole energies that a magnet transmits, a natural energy found in nature, were further evidence that genetics in nature could be altered. We believe that further research and development with magnetic energy in limb regrowth should be forthcoming. Research scientists may make discoveries. This does not mean that these discoveries will be acted upon and developed for further significance. A research scientist continues his work although his reproducible findings may be disregarded. This was our position some years ago. It is our position today. We search to find answers why things do or do not happen, improving knowns against unknowns. We explore the mysteries in life, if for no other reason than to better understand the known and unknown laws of nature. A better understanding of nature can aid life forms to exist more adequately in and with nature.

CHAPTER VI

MAGNETIC ANESTHESIA

The remarkable discovery of the negative North pole energies has been researched on hundreds of cases where pain exists. Magnetic anesthesia can be utilized in nearly all cases where pain is present.

Nerve cells differ from blood cells. This is elementary. Blood cells have potassium in their center, which has a positive bioelectrical charge. The nerve cells differ in this respect; the outside of the cell is positive and the inside has a negative bioelectrical charge.

Separating the North pole of all magnets from the South pole, more readily accomplished using a cylinder or bar magnet with a separate pole on each end or side, furnishes a negative natural energy of nature. Electronic tests show the North pole energy as negative versus the South pole energy as positive.

Using established laws in electrical energy, we know that two like forces close together repel one another. We also know when two dissimilar energies (positive-negative) are brought together they attract to the other. Bringing two South poles of positive energy together would repel. Likewise, two North poles of negative energy would act to push one away from the other. We use known laws of electricity and applied physics for the resulting reaction occurring in the lessening of pain. The North pole negative energy is applied to sensitive nerves and their endings.

We are applying a magnetic form of negative energy to the positive biological nerve surface energies beneath the skin. Bringing the negative energies to the close proximity nerve cells and fibres, we act to attract the positive energies that are excited on the nerve surfaces. This also stimulates the biological bioelectrical energies flowing, passing, and being exchanged between the positive outer nerve currents and the negative surface energy of the applied biomagnet.

In the initial action of any electrical circuit, voltage flows between two dissimilar locations. Then a reverse action occurs with current flowing, which results in voltage and current flowing together. There is a separation of energies by a division referred to as the Bloch Wall. Our earlier book goes into more detail on the Bloch Wall Effect.

Positive electrical energy flows from positive to negative. Because the positive energy flows toward the North pole negative energy, a path is established for the positive electromagnetic energy existing on the nerves to be directed to the negative energy of the North pole magnet. In other words, there is a "bleeding-off" of the sensitive positive energy of the nerves to the North pole energies. This LOWERS the positive charge on the nerves' exterior membranes in line with accepted laws we can understand how a sedating reaction occurs to and principles of energy transfer and interaction. Thus reduce pain. This in turn reduces the sensation flow of energy to the brain. Because pain is a sensation to the nerves and mental processes, reducing this sensation reduces the pain. Therefore, we are actually reducing the volume flow of energy that carries to the nerve axions in the brain. This is magneto-magnetic sedation or anesthesia by magnetic application.

CHAPTER VII

MAGNETIC ANESTHESIA VERSUS ACUPUNCTURE

Although magneto-magnetic anesthesia is slower than direct insertion of needles into the body for pain control, as in acupuncture, comparison should be made between the overall beneficial effects of magnetic anesthesia and the short-term effects of acupuncture.

In the science of applied acupuncture, needles are inserted into the skin to touch and penetrate nerves, their axions, and endings. Shallow to deep insertions are used. Needles are also slid into the skin, then turned to follow a shallow interior under the surface of the skin. Selecting known acupuncture points to relieve active transfer of nerve energy to the brain is the basic concept of applied acupuncture. Relieving active transfer of nerve energy to the brain relieves pain.

Acupuncture also uses small flashlight-type batteries with wires attached to the needles in applying external voltages to the nerves. This is a further restriction on the transfer of pain sensation to the brain. This mechanism acts to adjust delivery in fixed amounts of direct voltages and currents. One positive needle and one negative needle are used. Some mechanisms have more than two needles.

Applying the needles to selected points of the body not only restricts the flow of nerve energy to the brain, but also serves to route the nerve axion active transfer of biological bioelectrical energies from the brain's receptor-receiver nerve endings in the hemisphere of the brain. Insertion of needles in acupuncture functions in much the same manner as having to detour during road repair or construction work.

Application of direct voltages and currents, in addition, supplies negative electrical energy that will result in definite reactions. Many specialists instructing and practicing acupuncture have little knowledge of the effects resulting from applying needles with voltages and currents to the human body. Many acupuncturists openly state they do not know why results are achieved. This is similar to many drugs that are used today. For example, medical professionals use aspirin for results, yet state they have no knowledge why results are achieved. How and why aspirin causes results is a research study in itself.

The research we have accomplished in the study and understanding of applied energies to the living system gives meaning to the effective use of acupuncture. However, the advantages of magnetic anesthesia, biomagnetic applications, are superior.

Acupuncture has no infection controls. Biomagnetics does. Acupuncture has no bacterial arrest, germ control, or arrest action. Biomagnetics has these abilities. Acupuncture is a corrective measure of limited duration. Biomagnetics has a more lasting result, in addition to aiding in the overcoming of the cause of pain.

Neither acupuncture nor biomagnetics acts in their means alone to heal or cure ailments or diseases. They do, however, by their application to the living system, promote and aid the living system's natural energies to overcome disorders.

Your authors believe this book's presentation of reproducible experiments and the findings thereto speaks for itself on the importance of biomagnetics as a new and vitally important method to relieve suffering of the living system. Biomagnetics requires no entering of the body system with needles, no miniature surgery. No battery mechanisms are necessary. Biomagnetics is a natural science that applies a natural energy to aid in improving a body system function.

CHAPTER VIII

MAGNETIC PULSATING EFFECTS

In our research on biological systems, we explored the effects of magnetic fields when pulsing or alternating. These fields generated by a magnet also encompass electromagnetic properties, alternating voltages and currents. Our research has been extensive in the study and reproduction of electromagnetic energies composed of fixed and variable frequencies. Frequencies are the number of movements, pulses or cycles of energy generated within a given time, herein referred to as C.P.S. for cycles per second.

All energy is motion. Without the spinning of the electron around the proton, the atom, as we know it, could not retain its form, shape, and energy.

When we cause the movement of any form of energy, there is a countereffect. The energy transmitted from a magnet is provable; yet the fact that this energy is in motion with a frequency is still not understood by major segments of the scientific community.

The frequency of the magnetic vortex form of energy a magnet transmits in motion depends upon the magnet's physical structure. Because the magnet's poles offer a number of magnetic vortex emissions, this presents a frequency of rapidly moving circular cables of energy. Lines of force, thought of today as the form of this energy, is an inaccurate term. We refer the reader to our prior publication, *Magnetism and Its Effects on the Living System,* for reproducible research on this new discovery.

Having an energy in motion with a frequency we can better understand we have a reaction energy by speeding the movement of this energy. For example, the energy of electricity, used to generate light and power, has a frequency, as used in the United States, of 60 cycles per second. If we take this energy of electricity and apply it to a winding coil, we have an electromagnetic form of energy. We have generated alternating magnetic energy at 60 cycles per second. With our knowledge of magnetics this means 30 South pole pulses and 30 North pole pulses per second.

The application of this simple form of alternating electromagnetic energy to biological systems can be extremely harmful. Properly understood and applied, however, there will be no harmful effects. The proper use of alternating magnetic energy can be of vital importance to all fields of science, including medical use, Correct application of energies from electromagnetic coils will dissolve human and animal capillary carriers in the body.

Sound waves and supersonics are waves very high in frequency. When generated and amplified to a frequency of 30,000 C.P.S. to 100,000 C.P.S., this energy can be concentrated to a point for removing tumors. Tissue that has separated, as we find in eye difficulties, may be welded together. Other delicate applications are possible, such as brain tumor removal without surgery.

Low frequency ranges of vibrations, like high frequency vibrations, will affect the minds of biological systems, including man. The brain of man produces a number of low frequency electromagnetic vibrations in the range of 4 to 7 to 14 to 28 to 32 C.P.S. If you were to generate these frequencies and apply them to the brain or body of man you would cause great harm to man's mental processes. The same harm would apply when using low frequencies on biological systems other than man. Here, also, the proper use of these low frequency vibrations can be useful and not harmful to the biological system.

Little is known by many scientists and laymen about our government's action to control the generation of vibrations. Occasionally we hear of some specific instance, such as the SST airliner controversy. It is a fact that President Lyndon Johnson, as one of his last acts as president, signed a law giving the Department of Health, Education and Welfare standby authority to regulate and control most, if not all, generations of vibrations. This is an all-encompassing field of regulation. It involves electromagnetic, sonic, microwaves, radar energies, light frequencies, even physical vibrations. It covers frequencies from a fraction of one to the higher known and yet unknown frequencies of matter.

This law could be applied to the making of a harmonica, the design and scale of flashlights, or the tapping of your finger on a table. The apparent infringement on the rights of citizens was faced with knowledge that a few nations of the world have developed frequency weapons that will kill or maim biological systems. What may appear as a harmless squeak of a door hinge, the sound of an attic fan, the scrape of a stick against pavement, if amplified, filtered and controlled, could kill or render unconsciousness. And the frequency could be inaudible to the human ear. Distances are not a hindrance. Frequencies can be controlled up to hundreds of miles and beyond. In the event you hear of the enforcement of this law you may now better understand why government control is necessary.

The existence of poor communication between government agencies and the public is well known. Scientific agencies and departments in our government do not adequately inform and advise the public concerning their research developments. The cloak of national security is a catchall allowing this behavior with no proper periodic assessment to determine what information can be released when not of further importance to security. As a result, we have research advances of great importance that should be released to the private sector. From the grade level of education through college levels, the lack of release of scientific information hinders the proper education of scientists in the private sector. From our documentation we find also that the government scientific agencies are not as familiar with scientific advances in other countries as their responsibilities demand they should be.

For example, the National Science Foundation indicated they had not known of 15 years of public disclosure by the Canadian government on the effective treatment of plant seeds with magnetics. NASA, the United States scientific agency responsible for sending astronauts into space, was not concerned about the magnetic effects in space on astronauts. They confirmed no research in this field, although the Russian government has for more than 10 years published information on their research in this area. We find this problem of communication and knowledge of nonclassified scientific information not restricted to the United States, but existing in many countries, according to our studies we have surveyed and documented. This problem also applies to the United Nations. For example, the FAO, responsible for administering the food program through the United Nations for starving peoples in the world, had no knowledge of the Canadian government research that increased plant and crop yield 8 to 12 percent with magnetics. Therefore, when we presented our discovery in magnetics to the United Nations free of charge that would increase plant and crop yields 20 percent or more, we were met with disbelief as well as the customary bureaucratic delays and entanglements.

Experience, as well as history, dictates the significance of a well-informed public. Regardless of the government system, when the people have the information, the facts, showing how they and their government can benefit, especially when not harmful, then the people speak and government responds. Delays are inevitable, but there has never been an instance in this regard in history that has not eventually been successful. The science of biomagnetics demands its acceptance for its benefits to humanity as well as the knowledge presented that could prevent further catastrophes in the environment and among peoples in this world.

For more than 30 years our laboratories have researched forms of natural energies and their effects on the life, will, mind, and physical body of biological systems. Many lower animals have a biological system similar to man and woman. A number of our findings in animal research are already in use on the human system by the accepted scientific community. Our continued research and findings indicate that the proper knowledge of natural magnetic fields will hasten adoption of this valuable science to aid all mankind.

We have shown in this book, this scientific paper with reproducible experiments, many facts that are new facts in science. There are also many facts presented known to many scientists but not to the general scientific community. It is also our position that these facts are of importance for the public to know. Knowledge must be acquired to be acted upon. Knowledge retained by a few cannot benefit as can knowledge retained by many.

Energy, motion, frequencies of vibrations are our environment and our life. Understanding the basic energies of life requires an understanding of magnetics, probably the basic science of all human knowledge.

The discovery of the two pole separate energies of a magnet, natural energies of our environment, is a basic fact to accept for further knowledge in this science. Accepting this fact, which can be reproduced over and over without failure, opens the door for applications into the fields of applied medicine, physics, chemistry, and perhaps all human knowledge. Proper usage is then the need to aid humanity.

CHAPTER IX

PROPER CARE OF THE LIVING SYSTEM

Animals, like man, cannot maintain good health if their activities cause ailments or complaints. The animal, like man, exhibits his health by the care of his body system. Neither can exist without a proper and sensible intake of nourishing foods.

Unfortunately, the consumption of foods having no or little nutritional value is increasing in our society. Complicating the lack of concern for one's health are the numerous books and articles written on natural health. There are perhaps more sick and undernourished persons and animals because of the many health fads than for any other reason.

Humans, as well as animals, although of different species, are separate, individual personalities. Society seeks to classify everyone and everything into segments. Biological personalities do not fit into square or round holes. What is good for one person may not be good for another. To follow any prescribed diet, no matter who the author or what the success of the diet, and without medical supervision, is dangerous and can be a sure path to death.

If a weight problem exists a medical doctor should be consulted. There should be a medical examination, for the cause, as in other instances, may have a physical or emotional basis. Medical specialists will tell you that correcting a physical or emotional cause will affect what you eat, as well as your digestion, and your metabolism will then function more nearly in balance.

Over 30 years of research work with animals shows little, if any, difference in this field from what the medical specialists tell you about your weight. This applies also to fresh air, a balance between work and recreation, exercise, and cleanliness. Animals are very similar to humans in this respect; our studies, however, indicate they seem to naturally know how to take better care of themselves than does the human system.

They may have a shorter life span than the human. For balance, the laws of nature provide built-in dangers in their natural habitats. Man also poses a threat to their environment by his introduction of artificial dangers. Unlike the overdomesticated pet, which is more like the human than the animal in nature, the animal in his environment seems more conscious of his surroundings and more aware of the natural care of his body system. We continue to be astounded by the perceptiveness of the animal creatures and their separate personalities in the world in which they live.

Animals, like man, live in an electromagnetic environment, continually bombarded with visible and invisible electromagnetic energies that affect behavior, health, and welfare. Positive and negative ions, similar to the South and North poles of a magnet, are always present, one form usually more prominent than the other at any given time. Proper care of the living system is necessary to cope with this ever-changing environment. When the environment is polluted, in a general sense, the ratio of oxygen, nitrogen, and other elements changes drastically for short or long durations. Diminished oxygen to the living system, caused by these environmental changes and increasingly aggravated by man, often produces effects on the system similar to those of alcohol, which also lowers intake of oxygen to the brain. A more natural existence should be sought with nature for animals, as well as man, not to develop into mutants through genetic changes. We mention this danger to all biological systems because the care of the living system is our subject. The reader may wish to consult our laboratories for more detailed studies on environmental changes affecting biological systems. Our research findings with magnetism, the basic energies of all life, strengthen our belief that we face a clear and present danger in the changing environment. Your authors feel compelled to give you their opinion in this regard, in consideration of our many years of research into effects on living systems.

Diet fads are common to animals as well as humans. Many natural food experts have appeared on television and written in books that animals would soon die if fed only white bread. They say the white bread on the market is worthless for the animals. Perhaps they imply the same is true for humans. In controlled laboratory tests, for two months, we fed 200 white rats and a number of mice and rabbits no food other than the commercially available white bread. No weight, color of hair, fur, size, or general health pattern was affected in any way with these animals.

Tests were also made at different times with the same animals to distinguish any difference in their systems with the intake of sea salt or standard table salt. Recorded reactions within two months showed no differences we could find that were caused by the type of salt. Diets of nuts of all kinds were tested. As a result, we noted an upgrade in stomach disorders from poor digestion. In some instances kidney stones developed. Squirrels, and other animals used to chewing nuts, are not affected as our animals were.

If you notice, squirrels chew nuts until the food is a creamlike substance before swallowing. Here the human animal should pay attention to this simple law of nature: Chew your food well before swallowing. The human system is not adjusted to accept, eat, or digest many foods that nature's animals can properly eat and digest.

Nonsensible diets should be avoided. Fruits and vegetables in balanced amounts with nourishing meats, cheeses, and fish maintain good health. Don't endanger your health with some new diet without proper medical supervision.

The animal body, like that of man, is a precise functioning biological system. This system functions with a balance of natural energies. An imbalance of the system is related to a physical or an emotional cause, or a combination of both. When the system cannot maintain its own balance of natural energies, we have found, in animal research, that the natural energies of a magnet, similar to natural energies in the biological system, will aid to correct that imbalance. If there is not proper care of the living system, then imbalances will continue to occur, regardless of the aid and assistance furnished to that system.

CHAPTER X

ANATOMY OF MAGNETS

SECTION 1. IDENTIFYING THE POLES

All magnets made today have a North and South pole. It is mandatory that the separate poles of a magnet be properly identified and marked for reference in biomagnetic research. Many manufacturers of magnets, as well as of textbook materials, do not properly identify the separate poles.

The North pole of a magnet seeks a South pole; likewise, a South pole seeks a North pole. The North pole of a magnet is not the North-seeking pole, nor is the South pole the South-seeking pole. In fact, the North-seeking pole of a magnet is actually the South pole. The South-seeking pole of a magnet is the North pole. The rule to remember is opposites attract and similars repel.

Test a magnet for correct usage by identifying the separate poles correctly. Using a bar or cylinder magnet, tie a thread around the exact center of the magnet, with the thread having a loose end. Tie the loose end of the thread to any stationary overhang that allows the magnet to turn without hindrance in space. When the magnet stops turning, the end of the magnet pointing in the direction of the earth's North pole is the South pole of the magnet. You may need a simple compass to determine the earth's North pole direction.

After you have determined the South pole of the magnet, mark that pole end with red fingernail polish or paint. Once you have one magnet properly identified for North and South poles this magnet can be used to identify the North and South poles of other magnets. For example, if we bring the South pole of any magnet up to another magnet's pole, a repelling force shows that the pole of the unknown magnet is the South pole. An attracting force shows that the unknown pole is the North pole.

You may wish to purchase a small inexpensive magnetometer. The sensitive needle of this instrument moves in one direction or the other depending on the separate magnetic pole in close vicinity. The law of magnetism is a primary law of nature: Like forces repel—unlike forces attract.

SECTION 2. STRENGTH MEASUREMENTS OF MAGNETS

The strength of a magnet, its power and energy, is measured in Gauss units. Gauss is the descriptive symbol for measuring magnetism, as the volt is the descriptive symbol for measuring voltage.

Magnets available commercially are not normally

sold according to their gauss strength. Instead, they are usually sold by their lifting power. For example, a horseshoe magnet is offered having a lifting power, when placed against a piece of heavy metal, of 2 pounds to 25 pounds to 50 pounds, depending on the size, type, or kind of magnet.

For our research, our laboratories have designed types and sizes of magnets as well as engineered many types of instruments to measure gauss. One of these instruments we use is a hand-held magnetometer. It is about the size of a pocketwatch and is self-powered. It can also be used to determine the North and South poles of a magnet. More expensive instruments are available from manufacturers. For research purposes our laboratories will help you acquire these smaller instruments if you have difficulty in obtaining them from a manufacturer. Our address is in the latter part of this publication.

As a guide to the approximate gauss of commercial magnets, consider the following: A magnet having a lifting power of 2 pounds may vary from 500 to 600 gauss units; lifting power of 5 pounds may vary from 900 to 1200 gauss; lifting power of 25 pounds is usually around 2000 gauss; with 50-pound lifting power, 3500 to 4500 gauss. For more precise measurement an equipment aid, such as a magnetometer, should be employed.

The energy of the magnet used in research should be known. The magnet should be designed to provide ONLY that pole energy required for this research. Many available magnets are incorrectly marked. Care must be used to properly determine which pole is North or South.

The N-1 type biomagnet described throughout this research publication is available from a number of sources. Many manufacturers are changing their magnet types. If you are interested in professional research in this field our laboratories will supply you current sources for magnetic equipment.

SECTION 3. CARE AND HANDLING OF MAGNETS

Care is necessary to prevent breakage and small to total loss of power. Never drop a magnet or strike it a sharp blow. The magnet could chip or break and also lose some energy.

Never store a magnet in a very hot location, because most magnets in temperatures from 400 to 500 degrees Fahrenheit lose all their energy. After using a magnet (flat, round, or cylinder), placing both ends of the magnet against a structure of flat metal will maintain the original strength. This is known as a "keeper." The keeper acts to maintain the energy flow from one end of the magnet to the other, and in this manner no energy is drained from the magnet.

For the N-1 type biomagnet, and similar types of flat, wide-surface magnets, you can also bend a piece of steel, iron, or tin into a shape that contacts the two flat sides of the magnet. This closed circuit retains the energy without drainage.

Keep magnets away from one another. If placed where the poles of separate magnets repel there could be a "bleeding-off" of the energy. A loss of energy in this manner would be rapid.

SECTION 4. ELECTROMAGNETS ARE DIFFERENT

Very effective and powerful magnets are made by passing electrical energy through a coil of wire having a metal, iron, or steel core. However, there is a difference between the magnetism produced in this manner and the magnetism from a solid state bar or metal composition magnet.

Magnetism has a frequency. It also has motion. The rate of vibration depends on the size, length, width, and power of the magnet. Solid state composition magnets, such as metal, iron and steel, are constant in their rate of vibration depending on their structure. An electromagnet, however, may present a number of different types of vibrations.

Any kind of electromagnet has many turns of insulated wire. Each turn of this wire presents so many lines of magnetism. Actually, we have discovered that these lines of force are really *cables* of force, as explained in our earlier publication. However, a coil wound a certain number of turns has a different frequency from a fixed metal or composition magnet. As the coil heats, the resistance to the flow of current increases. Here we have a slow drop in magnetic lines, or cables, of force to a rise in force, depending upon the wire and core materials used for construction. Therefore, the vibrations supplied by the electromagnet are not as constant as those from the metal or composition magnet.

Our research has revealed that size, width, and overall length of a magnet governs frequency in electrical electron vibrations. This is a discovery not known by the general scientific community, because we have not published our scientific materials on this research finding. We are working on this discovery in the establishment of provable laws that we will disclose when completed. We feel confident this future disclosure will open new avenues that neither we nor the general scientific community could properly comprehend at this time.

CHAPTER XI

OUR RESEARCH VERSUS RUSSIAN RESEARCH

Russian research into the applications and effects of magnetic fields is considered to be farther advanced than that of any other nation in the world. During World War II they applied their knowledge in the treatment of battle wounds. Since that time their research in magnetics has been diversified to include individual areas, as well as medical, and in the last few years it has been extended to classifications for their national security.

Our laboratories do not have the financial support or the equipment and technical facilities that are available to the Russian scientists. The support of the United States government for our work is still in its infancy. Since 1945 our laboratories have been actively attempting to convince the United States scientific advisers and agencies that the study and application of magnetism is imperative for the betterment of future generations. Many of our discoveries, not initially accepted, are now in use throughout the scientific world.

Without adequate support for development, we have

seen other of our discoveries later developed by countries with more adequate facilities. Some of these discoveries, which should have been properly supported in the United States, were instead later discovered and developed independently from our laboratories in foreign countries and sold to United States manufacturers.

The lack of interest of the United States government, manufacturers, and scientists in the applications of magnetism has been appalling and totally inexplicable. While United States leadership in science has slipped to at best seventh in the world, we still see a lack of concern for the benefits of magnetic research, development, and application. England, France, Germany, Japan and other countries, in addition to Russia, are increasing their financial support and facilities for research into the mysteries of magnetism.

Although the Russian research is outstanding in this field, we are convinced that our private laboratories hold a commanding lead over the Russian scientific community. This is an astonishing feat, we must admit, because all our support comes from the private sector. We have never received any government aid or grants for our research. The advantage that we have, over more adequately funded research facilities, is our discovery of the two pole separate energy concept—with more than 30 years of practical applications of this discovery to many fields of human knowledge.

When the Russians adopt the separate pole system, which they eventually must do to advance their research properly, we believe our many years of experience with this concept will not easily be outdistanced. Our laboratories, facing the Russian challenge, will continue to release information we believe should be utilized for the good of all humanity. However, there are discoveries that we will not release until a better scientific climate exists for acceptance. Nor will we release discoveries that we believe could affect the national security of the United States.

SECTION 1. DIAGNOSING ILLS WITH MAGNETISM

In the 1950s we discovered that the sympathetic nervous system reacted in such a way to biomagnetic energy that electronic instrumentations could be developed to more efficiently diagnose human and animal ailments. We have designed and developed diagnostic instrumentations with magnetic energy that surpass any known system today. Japan and England will probably adopt this system prior to its acceptance by the United States scientific community.

We anticipate that the Russian scientists will also make this discovery. However, if their discovery does not include the concept of the separate pole energy then their discovery will not be precisely accurate. Our discovery of the separate pole energy allows computer-exact results from proper application.

Russian scientists have already announced that measurements can be made of the energy existing on each organ, segment, and part of the body, which allows an understanding of normal energy present. Knowing the normal amount of energy, diagnosis can then be made based on existing excessive or insufficient energy. For many years our laboratories have sought the acceptance and utilization of this analytical process by our country's scientific community. Each organ, segment, and part of the human system has a biomagnetic environment. Here, as in all physics, there are two reactions to any applied potential of energy. Applying magnetic energy will affect a decrease or an increase. For example, an organ's efficiency can be reduced or stimulated. While the South pole (positive electron energy) will upgrade the activity and strength of all living systems, the North pole (negative electron energy) will downgrade activity and strength. What may seem to be exceptions, on further explanation and understanding emphasize these reactions. For example, the North pole energy will reduce the biochemical activity of proteins and sugars in the life system.

Applying computer language to the effects of separate pole energies on the living system, we have a Go effect with a control, a Go-No-Go effect. This is not as North pole energies we have a No-Go effect. Applying both energies stimultaneously we have a stimulating effect stimulated by the South pole energies. With the effective as the full potential of the separate pole effect. For over 30 years we have found that the separate pole effect is superior to the two pole effect. We expect that Russian scientists will also announce this discovery.

SECTION 2. INDEPENDENT VERIFICATION OF OUR RESEARCH

On a confidential basis we have worked with other scientists, research laboratories, and medical doctors in this country and more than 18 foreign countries, excluding Russia. Many of our findings have been reproduced thousands of times. For any new discovery to be accepted, science demands that it be capable of reproduction anytime anywhere by anyone so qualified and equipped. Research facilities at universities in the United States and foreign countries have reproduced some of our findings. We have been instrumental in introducing biomagnetic sciences into several foreign countries. In 1971 we received acknowledgment from India by Prime Minister Gandhi for our work in her country. For over 15 years the use of biomagnetics in the clinics of India has aided thousands of persons. The governments of England, Japan, and Australia have officially recognized the value of magnetics in healing. Other countries are soon to follow.

The current space program in the United States has produced some outstanding verifications; we doubt that the significance is fully appreciated. When men leave the earth's magnetic field, they leave a magnetic cloak that protects biological systems on this earth from detrimental rays and forms of energy. Also, leaving the earth's approximate ½ magnetic gauss, man ventures into a lower magnetic field in space and on the moon, resulting in harmful effects to man. Vital life force chemicals were introduced into man's diet away from earth to offset the lowering of physical and biological energies.

Scientific records show that the earth's magnetic field is growing weaker as the years pass. Thousands, even millions of years ago, the earth was surrounded by a magnetic field far more powerful than the one now existing. Modern scientific methods allow determination of the earth's magnetic field strength by measuring radioactive carbons in ocean beds, volcanoes, and other ancient deposits. It has been verified that when large mammals and great beasts roamed the earth the earth's magnetic strength was very high. As the earth's magnetic strength weakened the large creatures of the earth decreased and smaller forms of animals seemed to exist. The facts indicate that the size of the animal, as well as its intelligence, was affected by the earth's magnetic energy. Here, it is noted, that the magnetic strength of the earth today, although approximately ½ gauss energy, is not constant. Magnetic energy fluctuates in some areas to higher or lower gauss. A recent government survey mapped these fluctuations in a two-year study. Nevertheless, the higher fluctuations were much lower than existed thousands or millions of years ago in earth's history. Magnetism is a form of energy and now, as in the past, affects all living systems on the earth.

Our research in magnetic effects on living systems

has extended into chemistry, physics, electronics, man's biosphere, and related fields of inquiry. Our findings show that magnetism can be valuable in many sciences and is not restricted to arrest and control of diseases or improvement of man's mental and physical development.

CHAPTER XII

DOES MAGNETISM AFFECT WATER?

Reputable scientists more than 12 years ago suggested that we should not release any scientific papers on magnetic effects on water. Their contention was that water is simply water, and no one can alter water. Present accepted opinions of world scientists still believe this outmoded concept.

Water *can* be altered. The resulting properties can be used to relieve and control a number of human or animal ailments.

SECTION 1. OUR METHOD VERSUS THE RUSSIAN METHOD

This is another field of magnetic research where the Russian scientists excel. For years they have used magnetically treated water (polarized water) in their hospitals. Still, their system is not as accurate or effective as the system developed by our laboratories.

The Russian failure to adopt the separate pole concept in treating water has limited effective results. Actually, with the separate pole effect, several different types of water may be used for desired effects.

The Russian hospitals adjust a container of water with a valve at the container's end, allowing drops to pass as speedily as possible, without approaching a stream of water, through the ends of a horeshoe magnet's two poles. This polarized water is collected and given internally to the patient, who experiences a feeling of well-being.

Our laboratories developed a more effective system by the understanding and application of the separate pole energy. Our initial research used the end of a bar or cylinder magnet, allowing water to be polarized by the separate energy of the North pole. Studies in our laboratories, later verified with willing patients in Puerto Rico, demonstrated that washing once a day with the North pole water relieved the condition of bed sores. Continuous application for several days to two weeks speeded the healing of bed sores, and limited recurrence of the condition. By continuing the application longer than two weeks, once a day, the condition would not reoccur.

We soon developed a better system for polarizing water. We obtained glass and plastic jugs with tight-fitting caps. We filled the jugs with plain tap water and placed the North pole of a cylinder magnet, approximately 1000 gauss energy, against the container. In 20 to 30 minutes we had a jug of polarized water. Later, experiments with tap water from different geographical areas were conducted. For the desired effects we were seeking, results were standard using water of differing mineral content. It was also determined that the water could be polarized in only a few minutes' application. Placing the jug of water on the North side of the N-1 biomagnet also produced the desired results.

Most persons experience a decline in energy in the midafternoon, making it difficult to exert the effort necessary to complete a task. We have personally found that we could overcome this letdown by drinking an 8-ounce glass of North pole water while relaxing for a few minutes. There is a desire to get back to work, a renewal of energy to accomplish the task. Supplying the North pole water to listless animals increased activity. They became more interested in their surroundings and were more active in their play. Our research is continuing in this field. Many experiments remain before more detailed results are announced.

SECTION 2. WATERING PLANTS WITH POLARIZED WATER

We find that the effects on water by a magnet follow earlier research upon biological systems. The South pole energy acts to encourage activity. South pole water will encourage growth activity of plants. However, this water should be applied at the roots only. The increased activity may be too strong on the leaves or foliage. There is no difficulty in the plant accepting South pole water if used on the soil for penetration to the roots of the plant.

SECTION 3. WHAT HAPPENS TO POLARIZED WATER?

Although the Russian scientists have not announced their findings in this regard, we believe that announcing our findings is in the interest of scientific development. Without much detail, which shall have to wait for our comprehensive disclosures, we will announce certain facts that are apparent from our research.

In our initial research on polarizing water we submitted samples of treated water to universities for agriculture analysis. The test results showed no difference in the water. However, we persisted, because our other magnetic research indicated that there should be a difference. We could see the results obtained with polarized water. How to explain it scientifically was the problem.

It was conclusive that normal laboratory tests showed no difference in chemical, acid, alkaline or other accepted means using standard testing of water. We then tested the amounts of hydrogen and oxygen in the treated water. Using proper controls, as always in our work, we discovered that the oxygen level in the treated water had been reduced. We further discovered that, while the hydrogen level had not increased or decreased, there was a change in the hydrogen ion electronic activity. The hydrogen ions (charged particles) were altered to a noticeably higher state of activity. Hundreds of experiments were checked and rechecked. The results were the same. We developed new instruments in our laboratories for further testing the behavior of the hydrogen ions in polarized water. This research has now progressed to the point where our laboratories can make available from water minerals and chemicals not available in their present forms found in ordinary water—all by magnetic treatment. This research continues in the areas of chemistry, biology, and agriculture.

Our research indicates that magnetically treated water can reduce the amount of dissolved nitrogen in water. This could allow water to be safer for human and fish consumption, especially if the water were stale or stored for any length of time. Our research indicates that we could remove nitrogen from rivers, streams and lakes, thereby decreasing the growth of algae. Algae grows by consuming dissolved oxygen, which eliminates necessary oxygen for fish life, resulting in the death of large numbers of fish species. Here we can foresee that magnetically treated water can be used to combat the dreaded red tides of invading minute biological life that kill millions of fish species. However, the present circumstances in accepting new scientific discoveries appear to prevent the use of this important discovery in the near future.

Any man or woman entering scientific research must maintain an optimistic outlook. Delays are inevitable, disappointments are many. Dogmatic skepticism is evident. Exploring the unknown, researching to make knowns out of unknowns, can be a life's work. Discoveries helpful to humanity are no more readily accepted than changes that work against humanity. However, change is inevitable. A scientist, knowing he is correct in his discoveries, should persist in his work if circumstances permit. Knowledge by few can become knowledge by many. Knowledge by many can become knowledge for the benefit of all.

SUMMARY REMARKS

Although this report only generally discusses some of our research in the science of biomagnetics, we intend to publish more details of our work in later publications. Our research indicates that the science of biomagnetics involves all fields of human knowledge. Although we cannot attempt to publish all our research, we will release further studies in fields of interest as the acceptance of biomagnetics permits.

Because man is a form of animal, we believe that our findings and experiments should also be directed to man by medical researchers, because many animals and man respond similarly to identical treatments. Development of the separate pole concept of magnetism presents for the first time in recorded history a method for computer-exact results upon proper application.

This report was not written for use or information to treat human ills. It is the sincere hope of your authors that publication of these experiments and findings will result in further research reproductions by scientists independent from our laboratories. For too many years the lack of proper investigation by the accepted scientific community on the separate pole concept of magnetism has resulted in the denial of a new breakthrough that all indications show can aid humanity. It is time that concerned persons not in the scientific community were aware of this avoidance. Public demand for proper investigation will, we believe, lead to proper adaptation.

To enable any man or woman properly equipped and qualified to reproduce our findings, we have intentionally omitted highly technical terms, physics, and mathematics in this summary report. Although our laboratories continue to maintain the lead in this research, it is doubtful that our position can be sustained against the increased undertaking of biomagnetic research in countries such as England, France, Japan, and Russia. Aroused investigation and interest with the proper knowledge, will, your authors believe, establish biomagnetics as a necessary and basic science for all humanity.

INVITATION

Should any researcher, doctor, scientist, student or interested parties wish to write us personally, we will endeavor to assist them within the scope of our knowledge and abilities.

Communications should be addressed to:

ALBERT ROY DAVIS RESEARCH LABORATORY
P.O. Box 655
Green Cove Springs, FL 32043
904-264-8564

Should anyone be interested in visiting the laboratory please contact us in advance so proper arrangements can be made.

ABOUT THE AUTHORS

ALBERT ROY DAVIS

Scientist, born in Halifax, Nova Scotia, Canada, June 18, 1915; parents, William Albert and Annie Agnes (Robinson), England. Came to United States, 1936; naturalized American citizen, 1936; attended University of Florida, 1936. Owner and manager, Albert Roy Davis Research Laboratory, Green Cove Springs, Florida, 1938 — ; writer technical papers radiological fallout, AEC, 1945-1946. Associate professor, biomagnetic sciences, Naihati (West Bengal, India) Research Center, 1964-1968; consultant to the board, 1965 — ; recipient of a number of honorary doctor degrees in science; Director of the Albert Roy Davis Aerial Phenomena Research Association and the United Science Federation, Green Cove Springs, Florida. Served under contract Air Transport Command, USAAF, Port Security division USCG, 1942-1943. Acknowledgment for work introducing biomagnetic sciences to scientists and doctors in India by Prime Minister, 1971; acknowledgment by industrialists in Japan on work to serve humanity through science of biomagnetics; author of many technical and scientific manuscripts on applied sciences, also over 370 general science courses used and adapted for grade schools, high schools and colleges in the United States and many nations of the world. Inventor. Developed methods of stimulation in milk products by application of magnetic fields and energies, 1965; methods of ecology studies to control nitrogen in water by biomagnetic molecular magnetic stimulation, 1969. Address for the Albert Roy Davis Research Center is Post Office Box 655, Green Cove Springs, Florida 32043. Phone: 904-264-8564.

WALTER C. RAWLS, JR.

Dr. Walter C. Rawls, Jr., Scientist, Lawyer, Author. Co-founder and developer of unipolar magnetics. Author of manuscripts in history, law, and applied sciences, assisted in the discoveries and granting of 41 patents. Additional patents pending. Co-author of books explaining technology of Bio-Magnetics. Member, American Association for Advancement of Science, New York Academy of Sciences, Federation of American Scientists, Explorers Club (N.Y.), Fellow of The International Institute of Human Sciences, Fellow of the European Medical Association. Admitted to practice law before Supreme Court of U.S., founding member World Association of Lawyers of the World Peace through Law Center, former consultant to UNIDO (U.N.), and to Barclay's Bank Intl., LTD., London Hdgs. Graduate Juris Doctor degree, advisory council Washington University Law School 1970-78. Nominated 1976 for Nobel Prize in Medical Physics, awarded several honorary science doctorates. Listed in Who's Who in Technology and American Men and Women in Science. Biomagnetic consultant to the New Jersey Commission on Science and Technology. Expertise: Environmental Sciences, Medical Physics, Magnetics. President, Biomagnetics Intl., Inc.; Vice-President, Biomagnetics Systems, Inc.; Director, A.R.D. Research Laboratory. married, Sheila (Kirsch), Doncaster, Yorkshire, England; sons Richard Wayne and James David. Address: Post Office Box 655, Green Cove Springs, Florida 32043. Phone: 904-264-8564.

GENERAL RESEARCH REFERENCES

H. S. Alexander, *American Journal of Medical Electronics,* 1 (1962), 181

R. L. Armstrong and J. D. King, *The Electromagnetic Interaction* (Englewood Cliffs, N.J.: Prentice-Hall, Inc., 1973)

G. M. Baule and R. McFee, *American Heart Journal,* 55 (1963), 95

M. F. Barnothy, ed., *Biological Effects of Magnetic Fields,* 2 vols. (New York: Plenum Press, 1964, 1969)

H. B. G. Casimir, *Magnetism and Very Low Temperatures* (Dover Publications, Inc., 1961)

D. Cohen, *Science,* 175 (1972) 664

D. Cohen, E. A. Edelsack and J. Zimmerman, *Appl. Phys. Letters,* 16 (1970), 278

R. Damadian, *Science,* 171 (1971), 1151

A. d'Arsonval, *C. R. Soc. Biol.,* 48 (1896), 450

Davis and Bhattacharya, *Magnet and Magnetic Fields or Healing by Magnets* (Firma K. L. Mukhopadhayay, Calcutta, India, 1970)

Albert Roy Davis and Walter C. Rawls, Jr., *Magnetism and Its Effects on the Living System* (Hicksville, N.Y.: Exposition Press, 1974)

L. D. Davis, K. Pappajohn and I. Plavnieks, *Bibliography of the Biological Effects of Magnetic Fields,* Fed. Proc., 21, Sup. 12, Part II (Sept. 1962) 1-38

J. W. Devine and J. W. Devine, Jr., *Surgery,* 33 (1963), 4

J. Driller, W. Casarella, T. Asch and S. K. Hilal, *Med. & Biol. Eng.*, 8 (1970), 15

M. Eibschutz, *et al., Nature,* 216 (1967), 1138

M. Equen, *Magnetic Removal of Foreign Bodies* (Springfield, Ill.: Charles C. Thomas, 1957)

M. W. Freeman, A. Arrot and J. H. L. Watson, *Magnetism in Medicine, J. App. Phys.*, 31S (1960), 404

E. H. Frei, *et al., J. Appl. Phys.* 39 (1968), 999

D. B. Geselowitz, *Biophys. J.*, 7 (1967), 1

W. Gilbert, *De Magnete Magneticisque Corporibus et de Mango Tellure, Physiol. Nova* (London: 1960)

W. Haberditzl, *Nature,* 213 (1967), 72

S. K. Hilal, W. J. Michelsen and J. Driller, *J. Appl. Phys.* 40 (1969) 1046

G. C. Kimball, *J. Bact.* (1938), 109

Ronold W. P. King, *Fundamental Electromagnetic Theory* (Dover Publications, 1963)

Alexander Kitaigorodsky, *I Am a Physicist* (MIR Publishers, Moscow, 1967)

A. Kitaigorodsky, *Introduction to Physics* (Foreign Languages Publishing House, Moscow)

Morris Kline, *The Theory of Electromagnetic Waves* (Dover Publications, 1965)

A. Kolin, *Evolution of Electromagnetic Blood Flowmeter, UCLA Forum Med. Sci.* (1970)

A. Kolin, *Physics Today,* 21 (Nov. 1968), 39

M. M. Labes, *Nature,* 211 (1966), 968

Arthur R. Lepley and Gerhard L. Closs, *Chemically Induced Magnetic Polarization* (New York: John Wiley & Sons, Inc., 1973)

F. T. Luborsky, B. J. Drummond and A. Q. Penta, *Amer. J. Roentgen,* 92 (1964), 1021

S. Maeshima, *Magnetic Healing Apparatus,* U. S. Patent No. 1, 421, 516 (July 1922)

J. Magrou and P. Manigualt, *C. R. Acad. Sci.,* 233 (1946), 8

Max Mason and Warren Weaver, *The Electromagnetic Field* (Dover Publications, 1929)

R. McFee and G. M. Baule, *Proc. IEEE* 60 (1972), 290

P. H. Meyers, F. Cronic and C. M. Nice, Jr., *Amer. J. Roentgen,* 90 (1963), 1068

T. Nakamura, *et al., J. Appl. Physics* 42 (1971), 1320

Alfred O'Rahilly, *Electromagnetic Theory* (Dover Publications, 1965)

L. A. Pirusian, *et al., IZV. Akad. Science SSSR Biol.,* S4 (1970), 535

A. S. Presman, *Electromagnetic Fields and Life* (New York: Plenum Press, 1970)

A. Rosen, G. T. Inouye and A. L. Morse, *J. Appl. Phys.,* 42 (1971), 3682

Symposium on Application of Magnetism in Bioengineering, IEEE Trans. Magnetics, MAG-6 (1970), 307-375

Vladimir Tahny (translated by), *Outer Space and Man* (MIR Publishers, Moscow, 1967)

J. A. Taren and T. O. Babrielsen, *Science,* 168 (1970), 138